D1614951

THE PHILOSOPHY AND PRACTICE
OF YOGA

THE PHILOSOPHY AND PRACTICE OF YOGA

by

James McCartney

Sketches by Keith Martin
Diagrams by Edmund Goddard

L. N. FOWLER & CO. LTD.
1201/3 HIGH ROAD, CHADWELL HEATH
ROMFORD, ESSEX, RM6 4DH

© JAMES McCARTNEY 1978

SBN 85243 355 7

Printed in Great Britain at
The Camelot Press Ltd, Southampton

Contents

GLOSSARY

List of Illustrations

Preface

I am grateful to my dear friend James McCartney for inviting me to write the Preface to his latest book. It is written around the examination syllabi of the Friends of Yoga (of which I am Hon. Organiser) and the British Wheel of Yoga (of which I am founder) and as each stemmed from my own ideas I am most happy to have some small part in making these schemes known.

"Fryog", the Wheel and the Yoga Society (in which the author and I hold Hon. Fellowships) insist on the whole Yoga being taught and not a mere part of it. It cannot be too strongly emphasised that Hatha Yoga, the physical-cum-mental aspect which is so widely popular, is but a preparation for Yoga proper, which is a way of life, physically, mentally, ethically, philosophically and spiritually.

Mr. McCartney has dealt with the subject in considerable depth from the general background of the life-science to the Goal Supreme – Realisation. I would take this opportunity of stressing that *every* aspect of Yoga has a marked therapeutic value for the very reason that it calms the mind and the entire system. So none should be omitted in public or private classes. The mind is, in fact, more important than the flesh body and the True Self within is the more enduring.

Dr. Burr has rendered yeoman service to Yoga in the Appendix by pointing out that science is only just beginning to discover what yogis have known for an estimated period of 6000 years!

The Friends of Yoga and the Wheel are members of the new International Yoga Co-ordination Centre of India which is conducting research into the subject and which recognises the importance of the training in both the U.K. bodies and the need for their examination and Diplomas. I wish this work every success; a most valuable book for teachers and students alike.

Forest of Arden   Wilfred A. Clark
Founder of the British Wheel of Yoga
Fellow of the Yoga Society
U.K. Representative of the International Yoga Centre, Bombay

Bibliography

The Works of Swami Vivekananda, published by Ramakrishna Mission

The Works of Swami Aurobindo, published by All India Press, Pondicherry

The Works of Swami Ramacharaka, published by L. N. Fowler & Co. Ltd.

The Works of Swami Sivananda, published by Divine Life Publications

The Works of Swami Ramana Maharshi, published by Sri Ramanashram

Yoga – the Key to Life, by James McCartney, published by Rider & Co.

Yoga Uniting East & West, published by Allen & Unwin

Himalayas of the Soul, by Mascaro, published by John Murray

The Upanishads, by Prof. Max Muller, published by O.U.P.

Practical Yoga, by Ernest Wood, published by Rider & Co.

Many Mansions, by Geminara, published by Neville Spearman & Co.

Hinduism, by Swami Nirvedanada, published by The Mission

Foundations of Tibetan Mysticism, by Lama A. Govinda, published by Rider & Co.

How to Enter the Silence, by Helen Rhodes Wallace, published by L. N. Fowler & Co. Ltd.

The Bible

Practice of the Presence of God, by Brother Lawrence, published by Burns and Oats

A Visit to a Jnani, by Ed. Carpenter, published by Rider & Co.

Shadow of Destiny, by A. Cannon, published by Rider & Co.

Asanas, by Swami Kuvalayananda, published by Popular Prakashan, Bombay

The Mind and Its Control, by Swami Budhananda, published by Advaita Ashram

The Encyclopaedia Britannica

ACKNOWLEDGEMENTS

My grateful thanks are due to the following publishers who have kindly given me permission to use extracts from their publications: Messrs. Rider & Co., Allen & Unwin Ltd., Oxford University Press, John Murray Ltd.

Also to Keith Martin for his excellent sketches of the asanas; Edmund Goddard for assistance with the diagrams, and John Antwis for the Spectrum of Electromagnetic Energy, and, by no means least, those Yoga teachers without whose enthusiasm and encouragement this book would not have been written.

Introduction

In response to requests from readers of my previous book, *Yoga – The Key to Life*, this book is presented as a study of the Philosophy and the concepts of Yoga in greater depth than was possible in the previous volume. Its intention is to trace the origin and purpose of Yoga, but, more particularly, to summarise the development of Yogi thought and literature, and their relation to life today.

Although Yoga has existed in India from times before the memory of man, its history disappearing into the mists of pre-historic Hindustan, the need for its practical teaching and disciplines has never been greater than in the world today. Torn by strife and dissension, the world appears to be motivated by greed and fear born of ignorance. Once this ignorance has been dispelled, and man lives in the full knowledge of his own true origin and purpose, then strife and dissension will give way to harmony, peace and plenty, and this is the knowledge which Yoga can provide in such clear and logical terms, that it is well within the understanding of all.

The restricting and schismatic dogmatism of organised religion has served only to turn people away from the churches, where the searching mind has found no satisfaction, but has been left in a vacuum of doubt. The immediate rewards of materialism have blinded people to the greater rewards of the Spirit, and to the absolute need to have regard for its Laws, for the Laws of the Spirit reach out into Eternity in terms of Joy or Suffering, according to the Path one has chosen and the way in which one has lived.

Whereas no single religion is able to attract all peoples, Yoga is not a religion, but rather a system of scientific instruction for the whole man, physical, mental and spiritual; non-sectarian, and therefore applicable to all. Its teaching begins with the simple physical instructions of Hatha Yoga, but expands with growing consciousness to embrace the Cosmic Whole. It is a well-tried and proven system of continued self-improvement, whose logical teaching shows, not only what one should do with one's life, and how to go about doing it, but also the reasons WHY. It shows the rewards of right thinking and right action, but also the inevitable consequences of their opposites, in clear terms of cause and effect, so much more convincingly than by mere dogmatic assertions. As the Spiritual Laws are basic to all humanity regardless of race, creed, age or sex, knowledge of those Laws will enhance and illuminate the practice of any and all religions.

Practising Christians might be surprised to know the extent to which the sayings of Jesus are used by the Indian Masters. Mahatma Ghandi frequently referred to the New Testament, and was said always to carry the Bible with him on his travels.

Yoga is primarily a science of Spiritual Realisation. It offers far more than a system of physical and mental culture which it is at times believed to be. Such are the mere preliminaries to a purification process which prepares mind and body for the later release of powerful spiritual forces which would otherwise maim and destroy.

In order to condense into one volume as much of the very wide scope of Yoga as possible, the book has been divided into two parts.

Part 1 gives the principal sources of Yogi Philosophy, and comment thereon has been kept as brief as possible commensurate with reasonable explanation.

Patanjali's Sutras appear to have been written originally as a system of "guide-lines" for teachers, an "aide-memoire" to ensure that important principles were not forgotten or overlooked. As there are now several excellent commentaries in circulation, giving the teaching in full detail, explanations here have been given only where the Sutras demand particular clarification, others being self-explanatory.

Part 2 is an attempt to outline applications of the Philosophy, and diagrams illustrating the text have been included. These show the principles by which mind may be directed to control and improve bodily functions, the principle of "The One and the Many", Reincarnation, the Eight Limbs of Yoga and the principal Asanas.

It is hoped that the wisdom the Scriptures together with the explanations of their applications, will give the reader a clearer picture of his own purpose in this great and wonderful universe, of which he is a vital part. How vital a part is entirely a matter of individual choice and dedication.

To my readers, whose letters from all parts of the world are a continuous source of encouragement, and to all those with a desire to KNOW, this further volume is offered in the hope that it may take its readers a little further along The Path, where the spiritual gifts of Peace, Hope, Health and Joy, may be found in the knowledge of Yoga.

Bournemouth   James McCartney
April 1975

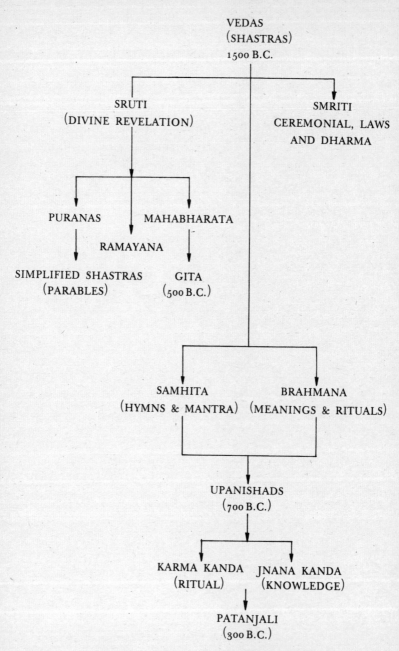

VEDAS
(SHASTRAS)
1500 B.C.

SRUTI
(DIVINE REVELATION)

SMRITI
CEREMONIAL, LAWS
AND DHARMA

PURANAS

MAHABHARATA

RAMAYANA

SIMPLIFIED SHASTRAS
(PARABLES)

GITA
(500 B.C.)

SAMHITA
(HYMNS & MANTRA)

BRAHMANA
(MEANINGS & RITUALS)

UPANISHADS
(700 B.C.)

KARMA KANDA
(RITUAL)

JNANA KANDA
(KNOWLEDGE)

PATANJALI
(300 B.C.)

Frontispiece: A Table of the Sacred Scriptures

Part 1

The Sacred Scriptures
and
Patanjali

CHAPTER 1

The General Background

Hindus claim their religion to be the oldest form of worship in the world, and there appears to be some evidence to support this claim.

Actual proofs do not exist, however, apart from the reports of archaeologists, for the sacred scriptures involving Yoga do not appear until about 1500 B.C. (known as the Vedic Period), the teaching having been previously passed on by word of mouth from Guru to Chela.

The same evidence may also be taken as valid proof of the existence of Yoga from earliest times, for the use of Mantra, Yantra and Mudra existed before the Vedas came to be written. All are essential to the practice of Yoga, and are inherent in the religious rites given in the Vedas.

Yoga therefore went hand-in-hand with the development of Hinduism, so that a study of the origins of Yoga must inevitably include a study of Hindu sacred literature which is its background, the fertile soil in which Yoga, as we know it today, has its roots.

Archaeologists claim to have discovered a civilisation which existed in the Indus valley some 5000 years ago, known as the Harrapas. With the incursions of the Aryans from the plains of Central Europe about 2000 years B.C., new concepts and ideologies were injected into the Harrapas' civilisation.

(It is interesting to note in passing that, contrary to the general belief, Swami Vivekananda always maintained that the Aryans originated in the Punjab, and did not arrive later as invaders.)

As the Aryan culture grew, and areas of cultivation spread across northern India, this region became known as Aryavarta, and as time went on, it was inevitable that Aryan activities spread beyong the mountain ranges. In this, one Aryan Sage, Agastya by name, is notable as having led one important migration southwards, which was instrumental in carrying the culture in that direction.

In the early days, the River Indus divided the Aryas and the Iranians, so forming the western frontier of the Aryas in the Punjab. The Indus was then known as the SINDHU, and so it was by this name that the Iranians called the Aryas. But the Iranians could not manage the correct pronunciation of Sindhu, rendering this as "Hindu", by which name the Aryas thus came to be known. As the races became more closely integrated, the Aryas themselves adopted the word Hindu, and so, with the spread of Hinduism to the south and eventually over the whole of India, the country became known as "Hindustan".

Until the present time, when western materialism and militant nationalism are making their impact upon the culture of the race, the people of India have been known for their instrospection, and for the controlling effect which religion had upon their lives and their culture. Looking back at the past history of India, it is evident that their greatest men have been philosophers before all else, thought and activity being sublimated to the dictates of the sacred scriptures, the Vedanta.

In the seclusion of hill and forest, seers and sages sought enlightenment in introspective contemplation, and they found all knowledge from a source within themselves. They found it true that "The Kingdom of Heaven lies within us". The concepts of Karmic Law, The One Creator, and similar concepts, were well known to the ancient sages (the Rishis), and their knowledge was passed on by word of mouth.

In the discovery of natural laws, the Rishis applied their knowledge to practical uses for the general benefit and to remarkable effect, not only in the field of philosophy, but also in engineering, chemistry, agriculture, medicine and astronomy, whilst a complex iconography developed over the years, which can still be seen in the carvings and murals adorning the walls of ancient temples.

The basic philosophy of Yoga is the basic philosophy of Hinduism, for the earliest seers who developed the practices of Yoga were the Rishis of the Punjab. From their knowledge of human biology and the human psyche, the Rishis formulated the movements and postures of Hatha Yoga with their psychosomatic relationship, and it is clear from the Vedas that the Mudras and Bandhas which are now accepted as an integral part of Yoga, were similarly an integral part of the religious rites and ceremonies of ancient times.

That same knowledge led to the development of mental control and the study of the mind in its process of meditation and contemplation, the turning of the mind inward upon itself in the search for the Real Self, which is a practice of Raja Yoga.

Devotional aspects led to the development of the school of Bhakti Yoga, whilst the knowledge of physical laws and their psychic counterparts, man's place in the universe, his relationship to God, evolved the Yoga of Knowledge – Jnana Yoga.

The sacred scriptures of the Hindus which give the teachings of the early seers, are called SHASTRAS, and contained in these are the texts which carry the essential quality, or the codes of duty, known as DHARMA.

All Shastras derive from the Vedas, which are held to be fully authoritative as they are the results of direct spiritual revelation (to the Rishis). Due to their unquestioned authority, the Vedas are known as SRUTI, as opposed to those Shastras called SMRITI, which are the codes of behaviour composed by later sages, based on the teachings of the Vedas, but carrying a bias of personal interpretation and application to local circumstance and belief. Not being "revealed", they therefore did not carry the unquestioned authority of the Vedas.

Those seers who, in different times and places attained actual Cosmic Consciousness (or Self Realisation), each found his own path to enlightenment, and he taught accordingly. In this way varying methods were developed, and in interpreting these to local needs and dialects, through modification and translation for different classes of people of widely varying standards of intelligence and education, many different classes of Shastras were the result.

The Vedas are claimed to be the oldest religious scriptures in the world. The word "Veda" is derived from the Sanskrit "VID", which means "to know", and VEDA can be translated as "Knowledge of God". The Vedas are concerned with spiritual life and include such questions as, "Who is God? What is His Nature? Where can He be found? How is Man related to God and by what methods can God be Real-ised? By what methods can Man find and develop the Divinity which is within himself?

What are the obstacles to be overcome, and how does one overcome them?"

Added to this formidable list are those codes of behaviour which teach the "Do's and Dont's", for the guidance of those who wish to travel the Path to Spiritual Attainment.

There are four Vedas, the Rig-Veda, Sama-Veda, Yajur-Veda and Atharva-Veda. Each of these have two main sections, the SAMHITA which contains hymns and mantra concerned with ritual and ceremonial, and the BRAHMANA, which give the meaning of the hymns and details of their application to specific rites and occasions.

Worship in the old days, mainly took the form of sacrificial offerings and oblation by fire. This form of worship is known as YAJNA (which is Sanskrit for "sacrifice"), and this was accompanied by hymns and mantra of the Samhitas. The Brahmana described the various forms of sacrifice, and gave directions as to which hymns and mantra were to be used with which form of sacrifice.

UPANISHADS are certain portions of the Vedas, usually occurring at the end thereof. They contain the essence, or the principles of the teachings. As they deal principally with knowledge of the Spirit and how this may be attained, the Upanishads are called the Jnana-Kanda, those parts of the Vedas dealing with ceremonial and rites being known as Karma-Kanda.

The Upanishads are many in number, several being contained in each Veda. The principal Upanishads are named by Sankara as:

Chandogya, Kena (or Talavakara), Aitareya, Kaushitali, Isa (or Vagaseneyi), Katha, Mundaka, Taittiriyaka, Brihadaranyaka, Svetasvatara, Prasna, Maitrayana.

SMRITIS are the codes by which Hindu behaviour is regulated. The Smritis cover all the Shastras with the exception of the Vedas. Every stage of life is catered for by the Smritis, whilst every social group and station in life has been included. Even in domestic life, daily ceremonial is detailed and specified by laws which are compulsory.

The sole object of these precise and far-reaching instructions, is purification of soul and mind, the teaching being designed in a consecutive and ordered sequence so that step-by-step advancement to Perfection may be achieved, regardless of social standing or intelligence.

The Smritis of Manu and Yajnavalkya are of long standing, and have the greatest significance, but many others have been written to cater for different needs, in different parts, in different times. The Smriti of Raghunandana, for example, is more recent and applies particularly to the Bengali, but the time now appears to be ripe (indeed, one might consider it to be overdue), for a new seer to arise, to write new Smriti suitable to the age and changing circumstance in which we live.

CHAPTER 2

Vedanta

In the course of time, various sages gave rise to various schools of thought, each of which claimed its own adherents, but all of these derived directly from the Vedas.

The teachings of the various schools are known as DARSHANA and, of these, six are now accepted as the Six Schools of Indian Philosophy. They may be tabled as follows:

PURVA MIMANSA		– written by the Sage JAIMINI
UTTARA MIMANSA	(Vedanta)	– written by the Sage VYASA
SANKYA	(Vedanta)	– written by the Sage KAPILA
YOGA	(Vedanta)	– written by the Sage PATANJALI
NYAYA	(Vedanta)	– written by the Sage GAUTAMA
VAISHESHIKA	(Vedanta)	– written by the Sage KANADA

The six are known together as SHAD–DARSHANA.

The writings take the form of aphorisms (SUTRAS), which, being by nature terse (at times to the point of obscurity), require interpretation and explanation. Inevitably, therefore, many notes and commentaries have been written to this end, of which some of the most brilliant are those of Shankaracharya and Ramanujacharya.

One of the cornerstones of Hindu teaching (and so of Yoga), is the Uttara Mimansa of Vyasa, which is derived directly from the Upanishads and is known as the Brahma-Sutra, but that in which the principles of a certain type of Yoga were laid down, was that of Patanjali. This forms the basis of Raja-Yoga in particular, as we shall see later.

The Darshanas, however, were written primarily for the Priesthood and the intellectuals. They were complex and difficult to follow, particularly with regard to the age and the civilisation in which they were written. There is also the fact that some texts are purely symbolic, so that a direct literal translation would be unintelligible to all but the initiated.

For this reason the Sages wrote simplified Shastras called PURANAS, and these carry the vital messages in the form of story and parable. In these stories one may also glimpse some of the events occurring in ancient Indian history.

There are in all 18 Puranas, the better known of which are:

> The VISHNU Purana
> The PADMA Purana
> The VAYU Purana
> The SKANDA Purana
> The AGNI Purana
> The MARKANDEYA Purana
> The BHAGAVATA Purana

A part of the Markandeya has for its theme the worship of God in the form of Divine Mother (the Creative Aspect), and this has particular application on certain feast days.

Two of the most important Shastras are the Epics, Ramayana and Mahabharata, written respectively by the Sages Valmiki and Vyasa. They are really historic in content (ITIHASAS), but they incorporate also the principal teachings of Hindu Lore.

The Mahabharata is of principal interest, as it contains the Bhagavad-Gita, one of the most important of the sacred scriptures from the point of view of Yoga.

The Gita is indeed the most popular of all the Hindu scriptures. It is now universally known and has been translated into most modern languages, and just as the Upanishads contain the cream of the Vedas, so in the Gita we have the distilled wisdom of the Upanishads.

The Gita is of such vital importance to the Philosophy of Yoga, that we shall deal with it in detail in a later chapter. It can be regarded as a crystallisation of Vedanta Philosophy.

Over the years, differences of opinion, interpretation and ever changing circumstances, have brought about the development of different sects within Hinduism, as has happened similarly in Christianity. Although based upon the authority of the Vedas in the same way that the various Christian beliefs are based upon the Bible, interpretations are different, and have given rise to the concepts of Advaita-vada which teaches monism, Vishistadvaita-vada which is a qualified form of monism, and Dvaita-vada which is opposed to monism, and believes that Dualism is the correct interpretation.

Tantric Yoga also stems from the Shastras, and is particularly concerned with The Divine Creator as Power or Energy (SHAKTI). It has many forms of ritualistic worship, some of which, unfortunately, have become degraded by certain sects from the originally pure teaching, and this has brought some Tantric practices into disrepute in consequence.

There are a great number of Tantras, some of which have fallen into disuse over the years. Some 64 Tantras are still of importance, however, of which the following are the most prominent:

Mahanirvana, Kularnava, Kulasara, Prapanchasara, Tantraraja, Rudra Yamala, Brahma Yamala, Vishnu Yamala, Todala Tantras.

Devotees of Vishnu and Shiva follow the precepts laid down in the Pancharata Samhitas and the Shiva Agamas. As the Tantras claim to offer methods of simpler understanding more applicable to present-day needs than the ancient scriptures, so the Samhitas and Agamas do likewise. They do not claim the same authority as the Vedas, and although they admit no allegiance to the Vedas, they do not deny them. This attitude of "live and let live" is a mark of the liberal attitude of Hinduism and of Yoga in particular, which allows one to take from the teaching just what applies to one's personal needs, without prejudice or bias. A ceremony of initiation must be undergone before one can be admitted to these sects, but there is no bar to class or sex, and there is no distinction between individuals. Sincerity, personal merit and development are the principal considerations for acceptance and initiation.

There are over 200 texts in the Pancharatra Samhitas, but of the few which are in general use, the following are most used:

Ishwara Samhita	— (see also commentary by Yamunacharya)
Paushkara Samhita ⎫	
Parama Samhita ⎬	Ramanujacharya
Sattwata Samhita ⎭	
Brihad-Brahma Samhita	
Jnanamritsas Samhita	(also known as Narada Panchoratra)

Of the Shaiva Agamas some 28 are listed, each having a number of Upagamas, but many have now been lost or have fallen into disuse, so that only a few sections of some of the Agamas have survived.

CHAPTER 3

The Upanishads – The Principal Upanishads and their Meaning

We have seen that the principal teachings of the Vedas are summarised in the Upanishads, and a brief study of the principal Upanishads will enable us to put these in proper perspective with regard to their own intrinsic value, but with particular reference to their influence upon the Philosophy of Yoga.

A word of warning: There appears to be a current tendency to regard ALL ancient writings as an unimpeachable source of infinite knowledge of matters spiritual and occult. So often nowadays, one sees references to "the Ancient Wisdom", but exactly what this is, is very rarely defined, and it appears to cover the whole gamut of philosophy from the earliest days of civilisation, with particular emphasis upon the cultures of the east and middle east.

Although there is no doubt that wisdom is to be found in some ancient cults, much of it has to be extracted from a mass of literature, much of which is now irrelevant and could have no possible use in this modern age.

Some parts of Upanishads fall into this category, and it must also be remembered that a considerable portion of the texts are concerned with ritual and law which could only apply to circumstances which appertained at the time they were written.

It is true to say that purely Vedantic ritual has practically disappeared, and it is becoming increasingly difficult to find someone sufficiently versed in the meaning and practice of Vedic rites to perform them and correctly interpret them.

Also, symbolism draws a veil of obscurity over much of what is written, but this is intentional for two reasons. Firstly, the dangerous, esoteric nature of the knowledge made secrecy necessary, and secondly (though perhaps of greater importance), spiritual experience is in itself symbolic. No words exist which can adequately describe something which is beyond physical experience, beyond sense perception and imagination. Revelation has almost invariably appeared in symbolic form, and as an example we may refer to the Apocalypse of the Christian Bible. This is completely unintelligible without a proper symbolic analysis, and here again we are confronted with the possibility of an incorrect interpretation.

The word Upanishad itself means "secret knowledge" or "secret teaching", but as most of the Upanishads were written some 3000 years ago, one cannot expect them to apply to the same extent today. However, the basic motivations of human nature do not appear to have changed very much over the years in spite of the comparatively exalted state of man's development, so that, although most of the civilised world has advanced some way along the Path of Unfoldment, the spiritual knowledge and guidance contained in the Upanishads can still offer enlightenment, guidance and encouragement to the seeker after Truth. As Mascaro puts it in his translation, "The Upanishads are the Himalayas of the Soul", standing high in the world of sacred scripture.

The Upanishads have creamed off the essential teachings of the Vedas, and if the Upanishads themselves are distilled, each statement then becomes a gem of true wisdom, a teaching of the highest spiritual value.

Philosophers, writers and seekers of all nations, have found inspiration in the wisdom and purity of the Upanishads, and the western world has Schopenhauer to thank for first translating the Upanishads from Latin texts into a European tongue. He wrote of "the vast treasures of thought which were lying beneath the fearful jargon", and openly admitted the profound influence which the Upanishads had exerted on his own philosophy, and many other great thinkers and writers of the west have expressed similar sentiments.

Although the Vedas themselves were handed down through the ages in unbroken succession, and in the earliest days this was by word of mouth only, it was left to the Persian, Dara Shukoh, the eldest son of the famous Shah Jehan, to translate the Upanishads into Persian about the year 1660.

At that time the Persian culture was flourishing, Persian poets and writers being famed throughout the world. So it was that, through Dara Shukoh, the Upanishads became known and appreciated throughout the eastern hemisphere, and then being introduced into Europe by those European scholars familiar with the Persian tongue.

It was the Frenchman, Anquetil Duperon, however, whose translations from Persian into both French and Latin, which made the Upanishads accessible to the western world, and it was Duperon's Latin texts which were seized upon with such delight by Schopenhauer. Schopenhauer's high standing in the world of philosophy gave credence and first opened the eyes of the west to the treasures of the Upanishads.

Dissemination of the knowledge of the Upanishads in India did not occur until more than 100 years after the appearance of the Persian translation. The year 1775 saw the birth of Rammohun Roy, who was notable as the great reviver and reformer of the Brahmin religion. It was he who translated the Upanishads into Indian dialects, and so awoke, in India, knowledge and appreciation of literary and spiritual treasures which had lain neglected and buried for so long. This remarkable man, whose breadth of mind and depth of understanding can be gauged by his positive statement of his belief in the Divinity of Christ, was one of the great men of his time, and he had great impact upon the development of Indian thought, both during and after his lifetime.

We have seen that the Upanishads, containing the essence of the Vedas, are regarded as "revelations directly from the Spiritual Source to the Rishis", and it is in the sense of supreme authority that they are regarded in Indian Philosophy. The Rishi himself, however, is regarded only as the instrument for the transmission of the revelations.

In view of the fact that the earliest Upanishads are now some 3000 years old, as Professor Muller puts it, ". . . they must be among the most outstanding productions of the human mind in any age in any country". They are a milestone in the development of human consciousness, a breakthrough into the Higher Worlds.

According to Professor Webber, there existed over 200 Upanishads, and some duplication under different names has occurred at various times. But there are well over 100 different Upanishads still in existence, though it would appear that none of the original manuscripts now exist, our only records being in the form of commentaries, copies of commentaries into different languages, and notes upon the commentaries.

After so many years and so many translations, however, one wonders how much of the original thought has been lost in the difficulties of translation and interpretation, but the inspired work of Sankara in this respect, is thought to be the closest to the originals, and is therefore regarded as having authority.

Sankara lists the following as the principal Upanishads:

1. Khandogya
2. Kena (Talavakara)
3. Aitareya
4. Kaushitali
5. Isa (Vagasaneyi)
6. Katha
7. Mundaka
8. Taittiriyaka
9. Brihadaranyaka
10. Svetasvatara
11. Prasna

It would be of little value, in this book, to analyse each Upanishad in detail. For this, the reader is referred to the complete and excellent translation by Professor F. Max Muller (*The Upanishads*, published by Oxford University Press), or to the poetic and simpler translation by Mascaro – *Himalayas of the Soul*, published by John Murray & Co. Instead, what follows is the writer's interpretation of those sections of Upanishads which apply particularly to the study of Yoga.

The Isa Upanishad (Vagasaneyi)

In the Glory of the Universe one may see also the Glory of God. One may perceive the Glory of God in all things that live and move upon the earth.

Thoughts of envy and greed must be abandoned, for these can only result in binding the soul to earth.

Abandon, then, the fleeting joys of this world, be not covetous, and look for the Infinite Joy which can only be found in the Eternal.

All actions should be carried out in the name of God, so that in this, the soul will find freedom and there will be no binding.

Evil worlds exist where there is only utter darkness.

To these demon-haunted worlds, after death, go those who deny the Spirit in this world.

Mind moves swifter than body, but Spirit moves swifter than mind and yet moves not. God is beyond the reach of man's sense perceptions. Though we may run, we are yet overtaken.

God is infinite and yet is close, He encompasses all, and yet is within all.

The Self is but a part of this great Unity, but cannot be known by knowledge or by action alone, but only through Union with Him.

Knowledge of that which is Immanent overcomes death, but knowledge of Transcendence achieves Union with Him.

When the Seer sees the Self as Unity and has knowledge of Transcendence, delusion and sorrow can touch him never more.

The Kena Upanishad (Talavakara)

This is a very brief, but important Upanishad, consisting of a dialogue between Guru (Teacher) and Chela (Student). It can be interpreted as follows:

Student to Teacher: "Who is it that sends the mind forth to investigate, who breathes life into the body and who gives the power of speech? What God is the Power which directs the senses of sight and sound?"

Guru: "It is the mind of the mind, the breath of the breath, the speech of the speech. When freed from the bondage of these senses (by Transcendence), the wise become immortal. That which cannot be expressed by speech, that which the mind cannot apprehend, that which cannot be seen by the eye nor heard by the ear, that alone is Brahman."

The dialogue then continues as follows:

Guru: "If you think 'I know it well', then you are deluded, for you can only know those things which appear before your senses. Therefore, think deeper."

Student: "I do not think 'I know Him well', but neither can I say, 'I know Him not'. He comes only to those who have succeeded in transcending thought, not to those who imagine that He can be known by thought. He cannot be known by learning, but reveals Himself to those who know this (Union) to be the true end of life. Those who do not know, are destined to continual rebirth."

The rest of this Upanishad is taken up with a dialogue between Brahman, the Supreme Spirit, and the mythical Gods Agni (fire), Vayu (air), Indra (thunder), Uma (Parvarti). This is intended to show that the Supreme Spirit is immanent in all the forces of nature represented by the Gods named, and is superior to them.

The Katha Upanishad

This is in several Parts which may be summarised as follows:

Part I

A pious man, Vajasravasa, was desirous of attaining Heaven, and gave away all his possessions as instructed by the Vedas.

His son, Nachiketas, though still only a boy, observing his father's actions, realised that, as a possession of his father, he too must be given away, and "faith entered into his heart".

Three times he asks his father, "To whom will you give me?", and at the third time his father turns angrily to Nachiketas and says "To Death".

To this Nachiketas replies that he goes to Death but in advance of those yet to die, and that he will be but one of those now dying. He then asks, "What work is it which Death must do through me today?"

In pursuing this question the boy goes to the house of Death where he resides for three nights, during which time "he received no Hospitality". When finally, after the third night he meets Death, to atone for his lack of hospitality Death offers to grant the boy three wishes.

The boy's first wish is that his father's anger be appeased, and that he will be remembered and welcomed by his father when they meet again.

This wish is granted.

Nachiketas' second wish is to be given knowledge of the sacrifice of the Sacred Fire "which leads to Heaven". This wish also is granted and Death is so impressed that he ordains that in future this sacrifice will be called "Nachiketas".

Death goes on to say that whoever performs this sacrifice and has been united with father, mother and Guru, and has carried out the three observances of study, sacrifice and charity, he will attain immortality and everlasting peace.

"This," said Death "is the chain of fire-sacrifice which leads to Heaven. Ask now, the third boon."

Nachiketas now comes to the important part of the Upanishad. "When a man dies," he says, "some say he still exists, and some say he ceases to exist. Teach me which is the truth."

Death replies that even the Gods had doubts on this point for the laws of life and death are full of mystery. "Ask another boon," says Death "and do not press me to answer this one."

But Nachiketas persists in his first request, for knowledge of "what is in the great Hereafter" and Death capitulates, giving him the teaching which can be broadly transcribed as follows:

Part II

Some things in life are intrinsically good (in the sense of spiritual goodness), whilst others give only pleasure.

Man has before him these two paths which are widely divergent, leading to two different ends. On the one hand there is the Path of Wisdom for those who seek pure Knowledge, and on the other hand there is the Path of Ignorance for those whose knowledge is only of worldly things, and who are like blind men groping in the dark. Theirs is the true Ignorance, and deluded by wealth and vain argument, they are unable to see the Hereafter, thinking this world to be all that is, and acknowledging no other.

These must suffer death (rebirth) again and again (until the lesson is learnt).

Few there are who can hear the Voice of God, even fewer those who see. Great is the man who can teach of God (from personal experience), and wise the man who accepts the teaching.

When the wise man meditates upon Self, as God who dwells in his own heart, then he rises above all joys and sorrows.

The Self is not born, nor does it die (it is eternal).

The murderer thinks that he has killed, the murdered one thinks he has been killed, but neither understand that both are wrong for the Spirit does not kill, nor can the Spirit be killed.

He who is free from desires and sorrows, by the Grace of the Creator is enabled to see the Self, which is bodiless, yet dwells within the body, is unchanging amongst the changing and never knows sorrow.

That Self cannot be known by thinking or by learning. The Self can only be known by he whom the Self chooses. Those who have not turned away from evil, whose minds are restless, can never be among the chosen.

Part III

The Self is seated in the chariot of the body, buddhi is the charioteer and mind the reins. The horses which drive the chariot are the senses, and the objective world is the road they travel.

If the reins are loose, the horses are uncontrolled and run riot, destroying the chariot, but he who is of pure mind, and has understanding, remains controlled, with peaceful senses, as well-trained horses.

QUOTE "Beyond the senses there are objects, beyond objects is the mind, beyond the mind there is intellect. The Great Self is beyond intellect.

Beyond the Great there is the Undeveloped, beyond the Undeveloped there is the Person (purusha). Beyond the Person there is nothing. This is the goal and the highest road."* Though the Self dwells in every man it is seen only by the seers of the subtle.

Strive then for all that is best and seek the light of knowledge. Wise men say the Path is difficult, thin and sharp as the razor's edge.

He who has known that which has no sound, is formless, tasteless and without smell, which cannot be touched and which cannot decay, which has no beginning and which has no end, which exists beyond the Great, he has attained immortality.

Part IV

Death continues his teaching:

The Self-existent created the senses to perceive the external world of objects, so that man looks outward and not inward where dwells his true Self. Wise men turning their eyes inward (in meditation) have seen their inner Self.

The foolish follow the outward world where fleeting pleasures end only in death. But the wise, knowing what is immortal and imperishable, do not look for permanence in the unstable.

This which makes us conscious of sound, smell, taste and love of beauty, by which we also gain all other knowledge, this is That.

When it is realised that it is the Self by which we are conscious in sleeping and waking then we can transcend all trials.

The world of objects is but a manifestation of the invisible for

* *The Upanishads* by Max Muller.

both are one. He who sees not the One behind the many wanders from death to death.

A smokeless flame, the size of a thumb dwells in the heart of the Self. Lord of Destiny, immutable and unchanging, this in truth is That.

Rain on the mountain running down on all sides may be seen as having different qualities, but as pure water passed into pure water unites as one and is the same, so is the Self of the wise man who knows.

Part V

The body can be likened to a castle with eleven gates (2 eyes, 2 ears, 2 nostrils, mouth, navel, 2 below the navel and one at the top of the skull through which the Spirit is said to depart at death). This castle is the house of the Self, and he who has entered therein is freed from the bonds of ignorance.

He is the sun in the sky, the air of the earth, the Priest at the Sacrifice and the Soma wine in the jar. He dwells in water, in the earth and in the mountain. He is Truth and is all powerful.

The Self is within all things, who creates the manifold from the One. To the wise who see Him in all things and who see Him within the Self, belongs eternal happiness which is denied to the ignorant.

Part VI

The universe can be likened to a tree which has its roots in the heavens and its branches growing downwards. All worlds are contained within the tree. Beyond this none can go. This is That.

The universe is born of His Will and lives within Him. The elements are His creation.

If a man knows Him not before the spirit leaves his body, he must then be born again in new creations.

As a reflection in a mirror, the Self can be seen within the body.

The senses arise from the elements of earth and are distinct and separate from the Atman. In knowing this a wise man gains control of his emotions.

Beyond the senses there is the mind, beyond the mind there is intellect, beyond the intellect there is the Great Self, beyond the Great Self is the Unmanifest all-pervading imperceptible. To know this is liberation from ignorance.

When the senses are stilled and the intellect is silent, the higher worlds can be reached. This restraint is called Yoga but care and concentration are needed or Yoga is lost.

The inner Self, no larger than a man's thumb abides in the heart of man. Let a man draw this out of its abode "as the inner stem from grass" (Mascaro) so that he may know the Self as the Immortal Light.

The Chandogya Upanishad

The first part of the Upanishad is taken up by derivations of various meanings of the sacred syllable OM. Some of the statements appear to be meaningless and do not make sense but the main intention is that while OM is being pronounced during the recitation of Vedic hymns, the various connotations of OM are to be held in the mind. There appears to be a progression of meaning from the unintelligible to the final and highest meaning when OM is equated with Brahman.

After this there follows instruction on meditation upon the Sama-Veda and the Sacrifices, but these would be of academic interest only and are not included here.

Three branches of the Law are then given as:
First; Sacrifice, Study and Charity
Second; Austerity and the practice thereof
Third; Dwelling with one's Guru, and mortifying the flesh

Then follows instruction on the various directions taken by departed spirits, which accord with the life they have lived upon earth and according to the knowledge they attained. Some follow the sensual path, the Devas, some the path of "The Father" (Creator), whilst others follow various paths, some of which are said to lead to Brahman.

The sixth section of this Upanishad is of great importance. Here, Uddalaka, the son of Aruna, instructs his son Svetaketa, who, having just returned from twelve years of studying the Vedas is "conceited", considering himself well-versed, self-possessed and strong in character.

Uddalaka asks, "Have you ever enquired as to that by which we hear but which cannot be heard, or that by which we see but which cannot be seen?"

The boy is unable to answer, and his father propounds the teaching as follows:

"By knowing one clod of clay all things made of clay are known, the difference being only in form and in name. The truth is that all are clay and their differences are only in words.

"Similarly by knowing one piece of gold all things made of gold are known, the difference being only in form and name. The truth is that all are gold and the differences are only words.

"Similarly, by one pair of scissors all things made of iron are known, the differences being only of form and name. The truth is that all are iron, the differences are only words."

Svetaketa then asks for further enlightenment, and Uddalaka continues his instruction as follows:

"In the beginning there existed only that One which had no second. But then, how could that which is (of the physical world), be born of that which is not (that which is not physical but is of spiritual nature). No, my son, only that which was and is, One only without a second, was the Creator of all things."

Various forms of creation are then discussed, and their threefold nature is expounded. For example, "Food, when eaten, becomes threefold. Its gross parts become faeces, its middle parts flesh, and its most subtle parts, mind."

This important paragraph summarises the teaching that Prakriti (physical matter) possesses the three qualities, or Gunas, namely Satva, Rajas and Tamas, meaning respectively the qualities of harmony, beauty and order (Satva), activity and emotion (Rajas), indolence, heaviness (earthiness) and inertia (Tamas). This threefold quality is said to be present in all things in various proportions and will be discussed in greater detail later, but it is important in the aspect of diet, when one must select those foods which are "harmonious and Satvic" in quality, so feeding the higher elements in man, and not the lower (animal) element. This latter, if indulged, can only lead to an intensification of tendency to passion and a binding to worldly things.

Two further lessons can be learned from the Chandogya Upanishad, and they are of the utmost importance. In spite of their brevity and simplicity, they summarise very clearly the spiritual nature of man.

The teaching emerges from the following dialogue:

"My son, fetch me a fruit from that tree."

"Here it is, father."

"Now break open the fruit."

"I have done so, father."

"Now, what do you see in the fruit?"

"Nothing, father."

"Now my son, in the fruit there is a seed, and within that seed is the very essence of that great tree. It is a subtle essence which cannot be seen, but it is the subtle essence of all things. The essence of that tree has its own Self, even as that Self which is within you. It is the same Self which pervades the whole universe, and thou, Svetaketa, art That."

"Please, father, tell me more."

"Very well, my son. Take this salt, place it in a glass of water and bring it to me tomorrow morning."

Svetaketa does so, and in the morning his father continues,

"Bring me the salt which you put into the water last night." Looking into the water Svetaketa, naturally, can see no salt. His father then says:

"Taste the water at the surface. How is it?"

"It is salt, father."

"Taste it now from the middle. How is it?"

"It is salt, father."

"Taste it now from the bottom. How is it?"

"It is salt, father."

"Now throw it away and come back to me later."

The boy returns later, and his father asks,

"Where now is the salt?"

"It is gone, father."

"Even as you could not see the salt in the water, my boy, so you cannot see the Self within you. And even as the salt was thrown away (with the water), yet it was not destroyed. So also is the Self. This invisible and subtle essence is the Spirit of the whole universe, and thou, my son, art That."

The Aitareya Upanishad

This Upanishad is devoted almost entirely to liturgical treatises, describing hymns to be used with certain sacrifices (the Mahavrata). Mythology and legend are also included, but the subject matter is irrelevant to our purpose and is therefore omitted.

The Kaushitali Upanishad

This belongs to the literature of the Rig-Veda, and contains statements concerning the passage of the soul after death, with some reference to reincarnation and metamorphosis. This, also, has no reference to our purpose.

The Mundaka Upanishad

The Mundaka is in the form of a Mantra, although not intended to be used in conjunction with sacrifice. Its object is to teach "the highest knowledge, which cannot be obtained by either worship or sacrifice". It has been called the "shaving Upanishad", as it is said to "shave off the errors of the mind".

A very broad rendering of the teaching would be as follows:

Brahma is the Creator of the Universe, and it is His Power which sustains it. The foundation of all knowledge was given by Brahma to Atharva, and this knowledge was handed down to Angiras.

As the holder of this knowledge, Angiras was approached by a great man of his time with the question:

"What is that by which, if it is known, all else is known?"

Angiras replies:

"There are two kinds of knowledge, the Lower and the Higher. The Lower Knowledge is contained in the four Vedas (Rig, Yagur, Sama, and Atharva), in speech, in ritual, in grammar, in the origin of words, in poetry, and in the study of the stars. But the Higher Knowledge is that which leads to the knowledge of Brahman (the rest giving knowledge only of worldly things).

"As the spider emits the thread of his web and withdraws it, as plants spring from the soil and hair grows out of the body, so does all else spring from the Creator.

"By diligent practice of the sacrifices of the Vedas, the Path is found which leads to Heaven. But those who depend upon good works only are improvident, and fail to reach Heaven. Those who renounce the world and practice austerities and faith, are freed from worldly traits and go to God.

"When passion and desire have been overcome and the mind is at peace, go then to a Teacher to find knowledge of the Truth.

"As from the blazing fire, myriad sparks, being the same as the fire, fly upwards, so an infinity of beings is brought forth by the Creator and thence return to Him.

"From Him are born Breath, mind, all organs of sense, ether, light, air, water, fire, and the earth which supports them all. He is the Inner Self of all things.''

In *The Himalayas of the Soul*, Mascaro expresses the next section with great poetry and simplicity:

"Radiant is His Light, yet invisible in the secret place of the heart, the Spirit is the supreme abode wherein dwells all that moves, breathes and sees. Know Him as all that is and all that is not . . . the inmost best of all beings.

"He is luminous and more subtle than the smallest, but in Him rest all the worlds and their beings. He is the everlasting Brahman. He is life and word and mind. He is Truth and Life Immortal. He is the Goal to be aimed at. Attain this goal, oh my son.

"Take the great bow of the Upanishads and place an arrow, sharp with devotion. Draw the bow with concentration upon Him and hit the centre of the mark, that same everlasting Spirit.

"The bow is the sacred OM and the arrow is the Atman, the Self. Brahman is the mark of the arrow, the aim of the soul. Even as the arrow rests in its mark, let the vigilant Self rest in its aim. . . .

"Where all the subtle channels of the body meet like spokes in the centre of a wheel, there He moves in the heart and transforms His one form into many. Upon OM as the Self, place your meditation. Glory unto you in your far away journey beyond darkness! . . .

"For spreading before and behind, and right and left and above and below, is Brahman, the Spirit eternal. In truth, Brahman is all.''

The Upanishad continues:

By truthfulness, austerity, right knowledge and abstinence must the Self be gained. That Self gained by the hermits is pure and is a light within the body.

The true Brahman shines forth, divine, smaller than the smallest, further than the farthest and yet near. It is hidden in the cave of the heart. He is not apprehended by the senses or by penance nor by charity. Only when a man is purified by knowledge is he able to see the Self by meditating on Him.

He who has desires is brought again to birth by those desires. But to him who has conquered desire and who has seen the Self, all desires vanish.

But that Self cannot be gained by knowledge of the scriptures alone, nor by other learning. He whom the Self chooses by him the Self can be gained. The Self chooses his own body.

If a wise man strives after the Self with strong endeavour, earnestness and meditation, then the Self enters the home of Brahman.

As the rivers flow into the sea, disappearing and losing their identity, so a wise man, freed from name and form, goes to the Supreme, the Greatest of all.

The Prasna Upanishad

The Prasna Upanishad is ascribed to the Atharveda, and takes the form of dialogue, in which six devotees ask questions of the Rishi Pippalada.

The Rishi instructs the six to "stay here a further year, living with faith and austerity and you may ask questions, and, if we know them, we shall answer all".

The First Question is:

"From whence came all the creatures that are born?"
The Rishi replies,

"The Lord of creatures was desirous of creating creatures, so having meditated, he produced a pair, matter and spirit, so that together these could produce for him a multitude and variety of creatures.

"The sun is spirit, the moon is matter, all that has form and even that which is formless, is matter.

"The sun rises in the East and so receives the Eastern spirits into his rays. Similarly when the sun illuminates all other quarters he receives all spirits into his rays.

"Thus, the sun, belonging to all men, assimilates all forms, as spirit, as fire.

"Thus, the seasons of the year are indeed the Lord and there exists two paths thereof, the Southern and the Northern. Those who regard worship as the true path (thinking this alone will lead to liberation) go to the moon and return again to earth. But those who have sought the Self in faith and abstinence gain, by the Northern path, the Sun, the home of the spirits. Here they reach immortality from which they do not return.

"Those who obey the Laws of Creation, produce a pair and so become creators. These go to the regions of the moon. But those who live in purity, austerity and faith go to the bright regions of the sun."

The Second Question

"What are the powers, those senses by which created beings are maintained, and which of them is the greatest?"

The Rishi answers,

"Those powers are the ether, air, fire, water, earth, speech, mind, eye and ear."

The argument continues, showing that Prana, the Life Force inherent in all the powers, is greatest of all.

"Life is the heat of the fire and the light of the sun, the wind, rain and thunder in the sky. Life is matter and earth, what has form and what is formless, and beyond this is Eternity.

"On Life all things rest, as the spokes of a wheel rest upon the hub.

"Protect us then O Life with that invisible essence which gives life to the ear, the eye and the voice, and which dwells in the mind. Dwell with us always and never leave us. Protect us as a mother protects her child, O Life, teach us wisdom and lead us to Thy Glory."

The Third Question

"Whence does the Life Spirit (Prana) arise? How does it enter the body and how dwells it there. How does it leave the body and how does it sustain what is without and what is within?"

The Rishi replies,

"Life emanates from the Spirit. (Prana is created by the Self) and as one throws his shadow upon another, so does the Spirit cast the shadow of Life which enters the body which is prepared (by good deeds) to receive it.

"As a King appoints rulers over certain areas of his kingdom, so the Spirit directs the powers which rule the body. Apana rules that below the navel whilst Prana itself dwells in the eye and the ear, passing (as breath) through the nose and mouth. The middle region is ruled by Samana and distributes the life-giving elements of food through the body.

"The Self dwells in the heart which has 101 arteries in each of which are 100 smaller channels in each of which are many smaller branches and in each of these the power of Vyana moves.

"Whatever thoughts are held at the time of death, united with the outgoing Prana (breath) and the individual soul, go to those regions to which its thought and deeds attract it.

"He whose light is extinguished comes to a new birth with his senses absorbed in mind.

"He who knows the origin, the entry, the fivefold distribution and the internal state of Prana, gains immortality."

The Fourth Question

"What are the powers that sleep a man, and what are they remaining awake? By what powers does one see dreams? What is that upon which all these depend?"

The Rishi replies,

"As the rays of the setting sun appear to return to that disc of light, and as, when the sun rises those rays re-appear, so are all the senses gathered into the highest faculty which is the mind. In similar manner man does not see, hear, speak, smell or touch and his normal functions lie dormant. It is then said 'He sleeps'.

"But the fires of the Pranas (life forces) are still functioning in the body and Samana is like a priest making the two offerings of inspiration and expiration. Mind is performer of the sacrifice and Udana is its fruit, since each day it carries the mind in sleep to Brahman.

"Even as birds return to the tree to find their rest, so also things rest in the Highest Spirit. It is the spirit in man which hears, smells, tastes, conceives and carries out all actions, and this spirit dwells within the highest, eternal Self."

The Fifth Question

"If a man meditates upon the syllable OM for his whole lifetime where does he go after death?"

The Rishi answers,

"The syllable OM is made up of three sounds A + U + M in which are both the transcendent and the immanent. Therefore he who meditates upon OM will attain one of these.

"If he meditates upon A only he attains only partial illumination and returns quickly to earth.

"If he meditates upon A + U he arrives at the regions of the moon and, being led by the verses of the Yajur Veda to heavenly joys, then returns again to earth.

"If he meditates upon A + U + M (which is the Supreme

Spirit) he comes to the highest light and is freed from bondage as a snake sheds its skin.

"Through the verses of the Rig-veda man enjoys the things of this world. Through the Yajur-veda he is led to the heavens, but through the verses of the Sama veda man reaches the Supreme, where he rests eternally in peace."

The Sixth Question

"Do you know that person which has sixteen parts?"

The Sage replies,

"That person from whence the sixteen parts arise is here within the body. He created Prana, which brought the elements into being. As, where the flowing rivers merge with the sea their individual identity is lost, so the sixteen parts are directed towards the Spirit, and having entered into Him, lose their individual identity to become that Spirit.

"That Spirit is He in whom these parts rest like the spokes of a wheel upon the hub. To know Him is to know Immortality."

The Taittiriyaka Upanishad

This Upanishad has three chapters, the first being devoted to Siksha (speech or pronunciation), the second to Ananda (bliss), and the third to Bhrigu. The chapters can be generally analysed as follows:

First Chapter

This begins with a prayer, or invocation, in adoration of Brahman, for protection and peace. Then follows the "secret meaning of the Upanishad".

Heaven and earth are united through ether.
Fire and the sun are united through lightning.
Pupil and teacher are united through knowledge.
Mother and father are united through offspring.

Then follows prayers for wisdom and happiness, accompanied by certain specified oblations.

In *The Himalayas of the Soul*, Mascaro translates the Ninth Anavaka of the First Chapter as follows:

What is needful? (to secure the Highest)
Righteousness and sacred learning and teaching

Truth and sacred learning and teaching
Meditation and sacred learning and teaching
Self-Control and sacred learning and teaching
Ritual and sacred learning and teaching
Humanity and sacred learning and teaching.

Satyavacas the Truthful says: "Truth" (is all that is necessary).
Taponitya the Austere says: "Austerity" (is all that is necessary).
But Naka, who is beyond pain, says: "Learning and teaching. For they are austerity."
The Teacher (of the Vedas) then instructs his pupil:
"Speak only the truth. Do thy duty. Study the Scriptures. Teach the children. Do not neglect the sacrifices. Do thy good works in secret. In charity, give with faith, with joy, with modesty and kindness. This is the teaching of the Vedas."
He who knows Brahman as the Primary Cause, as universal consciousness as the eternal, as that which is hidden in the depth of the heart and in the highest heaven, attains oneness with Brahman.
Brahman is the breath of life in all creatures, that same breath of life which is the embodied Self.
Brahman meditated upon himself and out of himself created all that is. He became both the manifest and the unmanifest, that which has form and the formless, that which has knowledge and the ignorant.
From the formless was born that which has form. It became involved with the Self and is therefore Self-created.
Therefore he who accepts not the existence of Brahman (God) denies his own Self. He who acknowledges Brahman acknowledges his own Self and gains joy and knowledge thereby.

The Brihadaranyaka Upanishad

This is one of the most popular Upanishads, having many translations, commentaries and discussions, containing, as it does, one of the clearest expositions of spiritual teachings, of which the following is an often quoted example:
During ceremonials these three verses are instructed to be repeated.

> From the unreal lead me to the real
> From darkness lead me unto light
> From death lead me unto immortality.

I am indebted to Messrs. John Murray for allowing me to include this beautifully written translation by Mascaro, which tells so clearly of that Power which is the real source of all attraction.

"In truth, it is not for the love of a husband that a husband is dear; but for the love of the Soul in the husband that a husband is dear.

"It is not for the love of a wife that a wife is dear; but for the love of the Soul in the wife that a wife is dear.

"It is not for the love of children that children are dear; but for the love of the Soul in children that children are dear.

"It is not for the love of riches that riches are dear; but for the love of the Soul in riches that riches are dear.

"It is not for the love of religion that religion is dear; but for the love of the Soul in religion that religion is dear.

"It is not for the love of power that power is dear; but for the love of the Soul in power that power is dear.

"It is not for the love of the heavens that the heavens are dear; but for the love of the Soul in the heavens that the heavens are dear.

"It is not for love of creatures that creatures are dear; but for the love of the Soul in creatures that creatures are dear.

"It is the Soul, the Spirit, the Self, that must be seen and be heard and have our thoughts and meditation, O Maitreyi. When the Soul is seen and heard, is thought upon and is known, then all that is, becomes known.

"Power will abandon the man who thinks that power is apart from the Soul."

The Svetasvatara Upanishad

Students ask "What is the cause which created all things? Whence did we come before birth? What is it that contains life and whither do we go? Ye sages who know Brahman, tell us who ordains our fate!"

Is man his own cause, or should time, nature, chance or the elements be considered the cause. It cannot be the union of any of these for then there must be one other to unite.

The sages in meditation saw that all qualities were inherent in God. Thereby He superintends all the causes and all the qualities and all there is.

That which is perishable is prakriti. The imperishable, the immortal, is God. Meditating upon him one is freed from illusion and ignorance, and when God is known, all suffering ceases.

Only that which rests within the self need be known for it contains all knowledge.

As the quality of fire is inherent in timber and has to be manifested with the ceaseless rubbing of a stick, so has the Self to be manifested in the body by meditation and mantra.

As oil is inherent in seeds, as cream is inherent in milk and as fire is inherent in wood, so is the Self inherent in man, and can be found by faith, good works and meditation.

If thou make thy dwelling in the love of God, then thy path through life will be without hurt. If a wise man meditates with erect body, and if he turns his mind to his heart, he will then, using the mantra OM as his boat, cross all currents of fear.

The Maitrayana Upanishad

King Brihadratha, having surrendered the throne to his son, left all, to go to the forest, having attained freedom from all desires and having realised the transience of all things of this world.

The Self-realised Saint Sakayanya came to him, full of the light of the Spirit, and the King, bowing before him, asked of the Saint, "Thou knowest the essence of the Self, which I know not. I beg you teach me this."

"That knowledge," said the Saint, "is obtained only with great difficulty. Ask me another boon, ask for other pleasures."

The King replied, "What use are pleasures to this offensive body. It is no more than a conglomeration of bones, skin, sinews, blood, flesh, mucus, tears, water and filth. Of what use are pleasures to a body driven by lust, greed, anger, jealousy and passion. Separated from loved ones, overpowered by those one hates, whose strength is broken by old age and whose body is racked by disease, of what use are pleasures to such as this.

"One sees our great ones fail and die, and all things growing and decaying, mountains destroyed and streams dried up. Who feeds on the pleasures of the world must return again to the world. Take me out then, from this world in which I am as a frog in a dry well."

The Saint, being pleased with the King's reply, then said,

"That which rises from the body when the body is in perfect rest, and in rising, reached the highest Light, that which then comes into its own true aspect, is the Immortal Self.

In the beginning, the Lord of Creation stood alone, but meditating, he produced many creatures. At first they were lifeless as a stone and without intelligence. So the Lord entered within them to give them life. As breath He is called Prana, as that which carries the nourishment of food to all parts of the body, He is called Samana. The five airs of the body are therefore Prana (the air which raises upward), Apana, the air which moves downwards, Vyana, the force which controls the two, Samana that which carries nourishment and Udana which controls excretion of waste. Between the Prana and Apana the Self produces heat by which food is digested, and when the ears are covered, the noise of the fire (Agni Vaisvanara) is heard.

Having hidden this five-fold Self in the body, He then, wishing to enjoy the objects of the outer world, opened the five senses (of perception).

Thus, the body is a chariot drawn by the senses (which are the horses) controlled by the mind (which are the reins) and driven by the whip of the passions.

Also the five senses (Tanmatras) are called Bhuta as also are the five gross senses. All of these together constitute Sarira (the body). The Elemental Self is called Bhutatma and is as a droplet on a lotus leaf which, though adhering thereto, is easily freed.

Because the Self is overcome by the qualities of nature (the objective world), he fails to see the Lord within himself, and so, vacillating between opposites and filled with desires, he is overcome.

If the Self is attached to the senses (sensual pleasures), it cannot attain the Highest.

Knowledge of the Scriptures and right performance of one's Dharma (duty) is the remedy.

By asceticism one obtains goodness from which the mind (now purified) reaches understanding. From understanding the Self is reached. The self-realised go to the Highest and do not return to this world.

CHAPTER 4

The Bhagavad Gita and the Four Yogas

The Gita has eighteen chapters which Professor Wood (*Yoga*, published by Penguin) classifies as Chapters 1–6 – Philosophical; Chapters 7–12 – Devotional; Chapters 13–18 – Practical.

The Gita is now universally known. It ranks among the world's greatest religious books and was written by the Indian Saint and Seer Vyasa some 2500 years ago. The Philosophy of the Gita is derived from the experiences of previous saints and seers, and corresponds closely to the teaching of Patanjali. It is generally in accord with the Sankhya Philosophy except in some fundamentals. The Gita holds that there is only One Supreme Purusha (Purushotama), and differs from the Sankhya also in its classifications of Prakriti. The Gita forms part of the "Mahabharata", which is in effect the history of an epic war between two branches of a royal family, the Kurus and the Pandus.

Jealousies and feuds between the two factions led to a great battle, the battle of Kurukshetra, in which it was said "All the Princes of India took part."

The Gita uses this battle as a vehicle for expressing spiritual teaching of a high order. The avatar, Sri Krishna, considering the cause of the Pandus to be the rightful one, chose to become the charioteer of Prince Arjuna, an outstanding warrior and champion of the Pandus.

Arjuna, however, on taking his chariot between the ranks of the opposing armies, sees in the ranks of the enemy, many of his friends, relatives and teachers. Appalled at the thought of killing them, he throws down his arms, finding that the strict rules which governed his behaviour as a Prince of the warrior class, the principles by which his life was ruled, have become incompatible with his love for family and friends.

Bewildered, dejected, and overcome with emotion Arjuna pleads with Krishna for enlightenment and guidance. Krishna first reminds Arjuna of what is his duty in accordance with the Law. He points out that if Arjuna refuses to do battle, "men will forever hold thee in disgrace, which is surely worse than death. The great men will think thou hast fled in fear; and those who have esteemed thee in the past will think little of thee in the future" (2–34/35).

Arjuna is not consoled by these arguments, however, and Krishna then begins to propound those philosophies which have made the Gita so widely known and loved.

Krishna first points out that the present situation has been brought about by the operation of the laws of Karma. In other words, the previous thoughts and actions of the Kurus and the Pandus have led inevitably to this confrontation. They are the direct cause of the situation which is now the effect. We are to learn from this that it is of no use trying to stand aside from events, as, somewhere in the course of time, the results of previous actions must be faced and paid for, so that to face up to situations as they occur is the only solution possible for our happiness and peace of mind.

"Thou grievest for those for whom grief is unnecessary. The truly wise grieve not for the dead, nor for the living" (2–11). Here Krishna teaches immortality; that which is the true Self cannot be killed, nor can it kill. These are terms which can only apply to the physical body.

"Know that the soul is imperishable" (2–17).

"Finite bodies come to an end, but that which dwells in the body and gives it life is infinite, eternal, and cannot be destroyed" (2–18).

"He who regards the Self as the killer and he who thinks it killed, is ignorant of truth for the Self, does not kill nor can it be killed" (2–19).

"It is not born nor does it die. It never cases to be. This unborn, changeless, eternal Self, cannot be destroyed" (2–20).

"The embodied Self casts off worn-out bodies and takes on new, even as a man casts off worn-out clothing."

"It cannot be cut by weapons, burnt by fire, nor drowned by water" (2–23–24).

Krishna then shows how birth and death are inevitable, and that the real Self never dies so should not be the cause of grief.

He points out to Arjuna that as his Dharma (duty) is that of a Kshatriya (warrior prince), "thou ought not to waver, for what can be greater for a Kshatriya than to do battle for what is right?" (2–31). "Those who are called to fight such a battle have, unsought, an open door to Heaven" (2–32). In other words, he who does his duty to the best of his ability inevitably goes to Heaven according to the Law.

This philosophy is the basis of Karma Yoga, as we shall see later, but in the course of discourse, Krishna expounds to Arjuna the fourfold path for attaining perfection and so attaining Heaven, and these are important to our study.

The four paths are (1) The Path of Action (which, as we have seen, in Karma Yoga); (2) The Path of Spiritual Devotion (Bkakta Yoga); (3) The Path of Knowledge (Jnana Yoga); and (4) The Path of Self-Mastery (Raja Yoga).

Professor Wood points out (*Yoga* Penguin edition) that further subdivision or classification can be made:

(a) Sankhya Yoga – Yoga by Science
(b) Buddhi Yoga – Yoga by Wisdom
(c) Atma Yoga – Yoga by Self-Knowledge
(d) Sanyassa Yoga – Yoga by Renunciation

The Gita, therefore, provides a basis for the whole philosophy of Yoga, but does not specifically mention Hatha Yoga. The reason for this is probably that Krishna is expounding spiritual truths, and therefore would not be concerned with those aspects directly appertaining to physical culture and physical purification, although there are essential preliminaries to the proper study and practice of all branches of Yoga.

The omission of Hatha Yoga from the Gita also serves to emphasise the fact that Yoga is basically a philosophy of the spiritual, rather than the physical, teaching how to reach the one through mastery and control of the other.

However, to revert to Arjuna's painful dilemma we see, even in the first few verses, a most important lesson which must be learnt by all, namely, that each of us must pass through a similar dilemma in which feeling (or Svabhava – one's nature) and duty (or Svadharma) are in conflict. Krishna teaches that without faith in the scriptures and a firm conviction that their teaching must be followed at all costs, we will almost certainly be led from the right path, to follow the dictates of emotion and desire. These can only lead eventually to spiritual destruction, pain and misery.

"He who acts according to his desires, ignoring the rules of the Shastras, will never attain perfection, happiness or Heaven, Therefore let the Shastras be thy authority and guide, and do thy work accordingly" (16–23–24).

"Exceedingly dear to me are those with perfect faith, devoted to the Dharma with Me their supreme goal" (12–20).

In the chapters which follow, Krishna expounds the philosophy of the Gita, the basic philosophy of Yoga.

Krishna teaches that there is only One Supreme Creator, who is eternal, immutable, omnipotent and all-pervading. He is at once the Creator, Sustainer and Destroyer, and Hindu Mythology names its deities in accordance with these and other concepts of qualities and action, teaching at the same time that the Supreme is transcendent to all such.

The Divine Creator appears to man in two principal aspects which are referred to as PURUSHA (Spirit) and PRAKRITI (Matter). Prakriti has sub-divisions which are referred to later, the principal of which is SHAKTI (Power or Energy).

In this lies an important point worthy of deep meditation, namely, that the physical body is formed by the Spirit, and must therefore reflect the quality and state of the Purusha. This is one of the fundamental laws on which the practice of Hatha Yoga is based.

Human sense-perceptions see an infinite variety in the worlds of forms and creatures. The "Four Kingdoms" of Creation, Mineral, Plant, Animal and Man, are infinite in their differences, for no two of any one species are identical. The Gita teaches that the Infinite Consciousness is latent in all Creation, throughout the Four Kingdoms, and it is brought to a state of individual awareness by the process of Evolution, in which we are all deeply involved.

Individual differences are brought about by the presence of three fundamental qualities, referred to earlier, the Gunas, Satva, Rajas and Tamas. That which is harmonious and bland as Satva, whilst that which is Rajasic is restless and filled with desires. That which is Tamasic is dull, inert and lazy.

These three basic qualities occur in varying proportions in every created thing, and so dictate their nature. It can be seen that all Higher qualities are Satvic, lower qualities are Tamasic, and Rajasic qualities shade between the two extremes. This differentiation is the basis of Yogic Diet, which teaches that bland foods and the subtle elements of all foods generally, go to feed the brain and mind, whilst heavy and spicy foods go to the lower organs tending to detract from spiritual qualities and aggravating desires, irritating the system. (See also *Yoga, The Key to Life*.)

The individual soul (or Jivatma), is a manifestation of the Supreme Power, the Para-Prakriti. The Apara-Prakriti comprises Buddhi, mind, the five senses, the basic elements (or Tanmatras), from which are developed all emotions, feelings and mental activities. The Three Gunas are present in all of these in varying proportions, as in all else.

The Gita states that there is only One Supreme Power, the PURUSHOTAMA. Purusha is the individualised Spirit, and Prakriti the lower element of matter and energy. But whereas Purusha is basically ONE, Prakriti consists of eight basic elements, from which there are fifteen further evolutes.

The eight basic elements are:

Buddhi (Intelligence)
Ahankara (Individualisation)
Mind
Five Tanmatras from which are evolved the principal elements of ether, air, fire, water, earth.
Fifteen evolutes of the basic elements are:
    Five elements of Perception – sight, sound, touch, taste, smell.
    Five elements of Action – hands, feet, speech, generative, evacuation.
    Five gross elements.

If one meditates upon the dual aspects of the Supreme (namely Purusha and Prakriti), it will be seen that, in the first case the mind is turned upon itself, and when all perceptions of the objective world have faded, then Unity with the Divine Creator is achieved, for He is seen to be all pervading and everything then appears as ONE.

With the mind turned upon the objective world, however, the infinite variety of forms is perceived by the sense perceptions.

Science has told us that all matter is composed of molecules, which in turn are composed of atoms, which in turn are composed of electrical particles. What lies beyond this science has not yet discovered, although even as I write, articles are appearing in scientific journals referring to even smaller particles than the electrons, protons and neutrons with which we are familiar. We appear to be crossing the border-line between physical matter and the world of mind and Spirit.

Similarly, when one looks at the universe and is told by astronomers that the Milky Way Galaxy, of which our earth is but one tiny speck, would take 100 million light-years to cross, then one is again confronted by infinity, for one light-year is 180,000 multiplied by the number of seconds in a year. Beyond the Milky Way there are even more Galaxies. The finite human mind is not built to apprehend the infinite, and we can therefore never apprehend The Infinite Divine.

The Gita makes it clear, however, that the Supreme Power, the Divine Creator, exists in the infinitely small (microcosm), as well as the infinitely great (macrocosm), as well as existing in all created things. From this, the concept of Unity is established when it is seen that ALL IS ONE.

The immutable and unchanging Godhead, the Gita calls "Akshara", and the mutable or ever-changing things of this world, the "Kshara" The Purushotama, however, is the Creator of both, is both, and is therefore trascendent to both.

A living being is formed by the union of the individual soul (Jiva) with Apara Prakriti (matter and energy). Because it is unaware of its divine origin, the individual soul, in its unawakened state, identifies itself with the world it experiences through its sense-perception the world of matter. The mental activities are almost entirely concerned with reaction to experiences and ideas, and so the soul becomes attached to the things of the senses, and is absorbed by desires and their gratification.

The soul is then in a state of ignorance (or Maya) but the Gita holds that the objective world is no illusion, but is a reality in the sense that anything which can cause a reaction of the senses must be real.

The Gita teaches that it is the attachment to the world of the senses which brings the soul back to earth in the cycle of birth, death, re-birth, until it achieves liberation (Mukti) by virtue of its knowledge, right actions and sacrifice. Krishna teaches that this state is only reached when Buddhi and all the elements which go to make up the whole man, have reached the state of purification and awareness in which the individual can be perfectly harmonious with the Divine. A state of Self-realisation then exists.

From this philosophy, it is easy to see the reasoning behind the Gita's emphasis on the two essential principles by which man must live, namely Svabhava and Sacrifice. Svabhava is the essential spiritual quality of the individual soul, and as we have seen in the distribution of the Gunas, each individual has qualities of different orders. Therefore it is evident that one individual has qualities which are either lacking, or are in diminished quantity, in another, so that to this extent, every individual has something to give to another and some need to be fulfilled by another.

Thus a state of mutual dependence exists, which when fulfilled in a perfect manner and without thought of self or personal gain, would lead to a state of world harmony.

This system of exchange is the basis of the law of sacrifice. The Master Jesus taught that "it is more blessed to give than to receive", the fact being that we cannot expect to receive until we have given. We must also remember that the laws which operate in our physical world also operate in exactly the same way throughout the worlds of Spirit.

In the later chapters of the Gita, Krishna expounds the main paths by which liberation (Mukti) is obtained. The Path of Action, we know as Karma Yoga, the Path of Knowledge, Jnana Yoga, the Devotional Path, Bhakta Yoga. Through the teaching and practice of these Yogas, ignorance is dispelled, knowledge and purification are achieved, and Realisation is attained.

The first step on the Path is a thirst for knowledge. Through this, refinement and development transpire. Also through learning, powers of concentration are developed, which are essential to the practice of meditation. Dr. Rolf Alexander has shown how the powers of a mind in concentration can disperse a cloud some distance away in the sky. What an effect such power must have on our own bodies and on our environment!

This, then, is a brief summary of the Philosophy of the Gita, and the extracts which follow will illustrate the teaching.*

* The sequence of verses in the Gita do not follow the same sequence as the subject matter. I have therefore extracted relevant text and verse and have shown these in consequential sequence. The figures on the left represent chapter and verse numbers or paragraphs.

Immortality

Chapter 2–12 It is not true that I have not existed before, nor thee nor all those gathered before us. Nor is it true that we shall cease to exist in the future.

2–16 That which is Real and which truly is cannot cease to be, even as that which is non-existent cannot come into existence.

2–18 Finite bodies come to an end, but that which inhabits and uses the body is infinite, eternal and indestructible.

2–20 This (the soul) is not born, nor does it die, nor, having been, does it cease to be. This is unborn, eternal, changeless, immutable. When the body dies, It does not die.

2–22 The embodied soul casts off old bodies and takes upon itself new bodies, even as a man casts off warm outer clothing and takes on new.

2–24 It cannot be cut, burnt nor drowned. Changeless and unmoving, the soul is eternal.

2–27 Of that which is born, death is certain. Of that which has left the body at death, birth is certain. That which is inevitable should not be the cause of sorrow.

Aspects of the Divine

10–20 I am the Self which exists in the heart of all men.

10–22 I am mind among the senses. I am the consciousness in all living things.

10–39 Whatsoever is the seed of all beings, that am I. There is nothing which moves or which moves not, animate or inanimate which can exist without me.

10–30 I am Time. . . .

10–33 I am the Eternal whose manifestations are everywhere.

10–36 I am the cunning of the gambler, the strength of the strong. I am resolution, perseverance and triumph I am the highest quality of the good.

10–38 I am the power controlling all who rule, the strategy of the conqueror. I am the silence of secret things and the knowledge of the knower.

10–32 I am the spiritual truth of all philosophies. I am the inspiration of arts and sciences.

10—23 I am . . . the mountains.

10—24 I am . . . the oceans.

10—28 I am . . . the thunder.

10—30 I am . . . the lord of the beasts.

10—30 There is no limit to My Divine Vibhutis (becomings).

The Spirit

15—16 In the world there are two Purushas (Spiritual Beings). One is the Akshara (that which is Immutable) the other is the Kshara (that which is mutable and individual). All beings are the Kshara.

15—17 But there exists another, the Purushotama (the Highest Being) whose name is Paramatman (the Highest Self), who is the Immutable Ishvara, who pervades the Earth, the Sky and the Heaven.

8—20 But beyond the Akshara there is one other unmanifested Eternal Existence, the Purushotama which is not destroyed even though all else is destroyed.

8—2 He is called Unmanifest, Immutable, the Highest.

15—18 I, the Purushotama, transcend the Kshara and even the Akshara.

9—4 All the world is pervaded by Me in my many forms. All existences exist in Me.

9—6 As the all-pervading mind, ever-moving and omnipresent, rests in the Akash (ether), even so do all existences rest in me.

7—7 Beyond the Purushotama there is nothing. All that there is, is strung upon me like pearls upon a string.

13—32 The Immutable Paramatman, though dwelling in the body, neither moves nor is moved.

9—9 Works do not bind Me (to the body). I am one indifferent and unattached.

Creation

14—3 My womb is Prakriti, into which I cast the seed. From this comes the creation of all beings.

14—4 Whatever forms are produced from whatever creatures, Prakriti is their womb and I am the Father who casts the seed.

15—13 Entering the earth with my Power (Prana), I sustain all beings. Becoming the sap in the earth, I nourish vegetable life.

15–14 Becoming the flame of life, I sustain the bodies of living beings, and joining with Prana and Apana digest all foods.

7–5 Know thou my Para Prakriti (highest) which becomes the Jiva (individual soul) by which the world is sustained.

15–7 It is an eternal portion of Me that becomes the Jiva in the world of life, and draws to itself the five senses and Buddhi (mind).

7–4 My Prakriti is divided eightfold by the five Tanmatras, Buddhi, individualisation and mind.

13–6 The five Tanmatras, ego, Buddhi, the two senses, the mind, and the five primal elements (air, earth, fire, water, ether) are the basic elements of Prakriti (Kshatra).

7–6 Know that from Purusha and Prakriti all beings are created. I am the origin and the dissolution of the whole universe.

Svabhava (Inherent Spiritual Principles)

The Gita teaches that inherent in all things, including basic matter, there is Svabhava, or spiritual principles or qualities which dictate the character or nature of the thing or substance.

For example, it teaches that the five basic elements, earth, air, water, fire and ether are responsible for the senses of smell touch, taste, sight, and hearing, respectively.

In general svabhava may be taken as the controlling power behind the *function or activity*.

7–8 I am the taste in water, the light in the moon and the sun, the sound in ether and manhood in man.

7–9 I am the scent of the earth, the light of the fire, I am the life in all that exists and the austerity of the ascetics.

7–10 I am the intelligence of the intelligent.
I am the energy of the energetic.

One's basic spiritual nature is the basis of one's character and duty, or, in other words, one's Svabhava is also one's Svadharma, for example:

18–47 Better one's own duty though imperfectly carried out, than the duty of another perfectly carried out. One does not sin when acting in accordance with the law of one's own Svabhava.

18–48 One should not avoid the duty to which one is born. All actions involve defects even as fire involves smoke.

Obstacles on the path of duty are the Gunas – Rajas and Tamas, the lower elements of Prakriti:

3–34 Liking or disliking the senses for their sensation is natural but beware of these for they are enemies.

3–36 Arjuna said "What is it which compels a man to sin even against his will."

3–37 Krishna replied "This is desire and anger born of Rajas, all consuming and sinful. Know this to be thy enemy."

3–38 As fire is covered by smoke, as a mirror is covered by dust, as an embryo is enveloped in the womb, so is knowledge covered by desires and anger.

3–41 Therefore from the beginning, control thy senses and slay the sinful destroyer of knowledge.

3–42 The senses transcend the objects of sense, mind transcends the senses, Buddhi transcends mind. That which transcends Buddhi is He – the Immutable Spirit.

Buddhi Yoga

Although rarely mentioned as a form of Yoga in its own right, Buddhi Yoga is fundamental to all other forms of Yoga. It is a higher form of Prakriti than mind, and is synonomous with Intellect, having the powers of discrimination, reason and decision. It therefore also involves will.

It is self-evident that the quality of individual Buddhi is of the utmost importance, for all experiences and sensations are passed to Buddhi for classification and discrimination, and it is Buddhi which analyses, comes to a decision and orders subsequent action.

Buddhi must therefore be understood, recognised and cultivated, and the first step in this is emotional control, for otherwise emotion will control reason and proper discimination and decision cannot take place.

2–60 The turbulent senses violently seize the mind of even a sage striving for perfection.

2–67 When the mind follows the senses, understanding is carried away, even as a boat is carried away by the wind.

2–62 When the mind is allowed to dwell upon the objects of sense, attachment to the objects follows. From attachment springs desire and from desire springs passion.

2–63 From passion comes bewilderment and loss of memory. From loss of memory Buddhi is destroyed. When Buddhi is destroyed man perishes.

5–21 When the soul is detached from enjoyments of the senses, the happiness which exists in the Self is found, an imperishable happiness.

5–22 Enjoyments of things of the senses are causes of sorrow. They have a beginning and an end and a wise man does not seek such pleasures.

2–64 The self-controlled man, free from attraction and aversions finds peace.

5–23 He who can control bodily lust and anger, he is steadfast and at peace.

2–68 When the senses are restrained from desires wisdom is firmly seated.

6–7 When self is conquered and serenity attained, then man's Supreme Self is steady and indifferent to heat and cold, sorrow and happiness, honour and dishonour.

2–66 For one who is not in Yoga there is no Buddhi. Nor is there concentration, and without concentration there is no peace there can be no happiness.

8–8 With the mind held steady with one pointed concentration, attained by the continual practice of Yoga, when a man meditates upon the Supreme Purusha he becomes united with that Spirit.

5–24 He who has inner happiness, who is at peace within and in whom there is light, he becomes Brahman and gains liberation.

2–71 Who abandons all desire, whose acts are free from yearning, who has forsaken the sense of "I" and "Mine", he attains peace.

15–5 and 6 Free from egoism, with all attachments overcome and all desires killed, freed from the dualities of joy and grief, the enlightened reach the Goal. Where lives the Timeless One.

Jnana Yoga

It will be seen that the preceding sections of this chapter are principally concerned with concepts of creation, the purpose of existence, of union with the Divine, and with general spiritual principles. Buddhi Yoga teaches discrimination and detachment from the objects of sense perception (in other words, from worldly pleasures). Self-control and concentration of the mind inwards in a spirit of intense love and devotion to God, are essential steps towards spiritual awareness.

The same teaching is fundamental to all religions, and all religions find the expression of their love and devotion in ritualistic prayer and sacrifice. The greatest examples in the Christian Church, are the Mass and the Rosary of the Catholic Faith. Buddhi Yoga is the intellectual approach which leads directly into the main stream of Jnana Yoga.

"Turning Buddhi to That, directing their whole mind to That and making their one goal That, their sins are washed away by the waters of Knowledge. They go to whence there is no return (to this life) (5–17). To those who are constantly devoted to me I grant that Buddhi Yoga by which they came to me (10–10)."

Jnana is the yoga of Knowledge, but it is stressed that the knowledge sought is basically Knowledge of the Divine.

"Out of compassion I dwelt in their hearts and destroyed the darkness of ignorance by lighting the blazing lamp of Knowledge (10–11)."

As an approach to spiritual knowledge, however, a knowledge of the physical universe is an essential preliminary, on the basis that, although we are unable to apprehend the Divine directly, it is possible to gain such knowledge by enquiry and inference. Once it is accepted that the physical world is a manifestation of the spiritual, and that, when we survey the former we are nevertheless regarding the Creative work of the Divine, then by knowing His works, we can know by inference, at least some aspects of His nature.

Universal mythology, for example, sees its deities as some super-beings endowed with greatly magnified human qualities, or as having those qualities generally recognised as "good", which are directly opposed to those human qualities recognised as "bad" – qualities which the human being aspires to.

In the Christian Church, God is seen as a super-normal "Father" figure, with greatly enhanced qualities of love and devotion, as the universal Provider, forgiving, comforting and sheltering from the harsh realities of the world in which we live.

The concept is generally anthropological.

Other creeds have a whole pantheon of minor deities to whom are allotted specific areas of activity such as provision of good crops, rain, sun, progeny and the like; to others are allotted the tasks of guiding the soul, after death, to its destination, the control of death itself as a prelude to rebirth (as in the cycle of seed-flower-seed), and similar functions.

All of these are human concepts, allotted to the Divine by human imagination which, in the uninformed and uninitiated, becomes a firm belief in the mythological as factual.

The knowledge sought in Jnana Yoga, however, differs inasmuch as, whilst it accepts the divine as having infinitely superior qualities to mankind, at the same time it postulates that, being Divine and therefore not human, it can have no human qualities, being above and beyond those things of its own creation.

Jnana Yoga therefore requires as wide a knowledge of the physical world as is possible for the individual to obtain, through this, a knowledge of the universal laws controlling the physical world, following which, through intense inner concentration and meditation, the Creator of these laws is sought in spiritual union.

The knowledge gained in study, experience and meditation, orientates the mind and elevates it to a condition in which such union becomes possible.

The preliminary physical controls taught in Hatha Yoga, followed by the intellectual exercise of Buddhi Yoga lead directly to that thirst for knowledge and spiritual experience which is given in the teaching of Jnana Yoga.

The Gita teaches that as in all things, Knowledge has the threefold qualities of the Gunas, namely that which is Satvic, that which is Rajasic and that which is Tamasic: Jnana Yoga is concerned principally with knowledge which is Satvic, that is, knowledge of the Divine as Creator, Sustainer and Destroyer.

"That knowledge by which the Eternal Being is seen in all creation, the One among the many, know this knowledge to be Satvic (18—20)."

"That knowledge which sees a multiplicity of forms only in their appearance and separateness from one another, know that knowledge to be Rajasic (18–21).

That knowledge which is confined to one single effect as if that were all, not seeing the true cause, not knowing the true laws, is narrow and is Tamasic (18–22)."

In other words, Satvic knowledge sees God in all His creation, the One in the many. Rajasic knowledge tends to consider things in isolation without regard for their relationship with all else. This breeds single-minded concentration in some but tends to fanaticism in others. The narrow-minded man, convinced that his ideas are the only right ones and tending to generalise on very limited knowledge of facts, he is Tamasic.

"That which is to be known, and which, by knowing one attains to immortality, that is knowledge of the Supreme Brahman (God), who is without beginning or end (13–13)."

He is without yet within all beings. Although moving He yet stands still. He is far yet near but is too subtle to be known (13–16).

He is the One, Indivisible, yet divided among all. He is that Creator, Sustainer and Destroyer of all beings (13–17).

He is knowledge and the goal of knowledge. He dwells in the hearts of all (13–18).

That Knowledge is gained from the teacher by question and service. Those who have realised Truth and have knowledge thereof, will instruct the true knowledge (4–34).

Knowledge comes through meditation in which the Self becomes known. It comes also by the teaching of the Sankhas or by the knowledge of works (Karma Yoga) (13–25).

By cutting with the sword of Knowledge, doubts about the Self which arise out of ignorance, take refuge in Yoga and do battle (4–42).

When ignorance is destroyed by self-knowledge, the Supreme is revealed within like the Sun coming from behind a cloud (5–16).

Separated from attachments, desires and fears, absorbed in Me and purified by the fire of Knowledge, many have attained to my Divine nature (4–10).

There is nothing in this world so purifying as Knowledge. The man who perfects himself in Yoga finds it of himself in course of time (4–38).

Possessing that knowledge thou shalt not again be misled by ignorance, for by this knowledge, those shalt see all existence in the Self and then in Me (4–35).

Perceiving the same Lord in all existence he is not hurt by ignorance of truth, and so attains to the Supreme (18–29).

When he sees the separate existences of all beings united in the One and emanating therefrom, he attains the Supreme (13–31)."

The necessary qualities of the man of true Knowledge, by which he may be recognised, are given in the Gita as:

"Humility, unpretentiousness, justice, forbearance, uprightness, service, steadfastness, self-control (13–8).

"Renunciation of sensual pleasures, absence of egoism, and denial that life, death, senility, illness and pain are evils (13–9).

"Non-attachment to worldly things or rewards, equanimity under all circumstances (13–10).

"Constant searching for spiritual knowledge, understanding of the true goal of knowledge (13–12)."

Bhakta Yoga

For those who "think with the heart" Bhakta is the Yoga to follow, for this is the Path of Devotion, taken by monks and recluses, who wish to devote their life to worship and meditation.

The Gita regards this form of Yoga highly, for "The Blessed Lord said: those whose minds are steadfast upon Me, who worship Me with earnestness and supreme Faith, those I consider to be in perfect Union (12–2).

"By devotion one comes to know Me, what are my aspects and principles of Being. Having thus known Me he enters into Union with Me (18–55)."

It is obvious that devotion and worship can be carried out for various purposes, but almost always it is for personal reasons that one turns to God. Disillusionment, suffering, bereavement, or even ambition, can turn the heart or mind towards that Higher Power.

The Gita takes cognisance of this, and Krishna tells Arjuna:

"There are four kinds of people who worship Me with devotion (1) those who are in distress (2) those who seek worldly gain and worldly pleasures (3) those who seek knowledge and those who have received that knowledge worship me with full knowing (7–16).

"Of these, that one with knowledge who is therefore in continual union with Me, whose devotion to Me is single-minded, he is the best, for he loves Me with perfection and is beloved by Me (7–17).

"Those who worship me, sacrificing the fruits of all their actions to Me and regarding Me as the Supreme Goal, meditating upon Me with single-mindedness, these I deliver from earth-bound existence before long (12–6–7)."

Referring to (7–16) and (7–17) in the preceding paragraphs we see in the first that there are four kinds of devotees, namely, the distressed, the pleasure-seekers, the seekers after knowledge, and those who have "arrived".

From verse (7–17) we infer that one type of worship is held in higher regard than others, and of them all, the Bhakti would appear to be held in the highest esteem.

The seeker after knowledge, the Jnani, is attracted by the Immutable aspects of the Divine, the Karma Yogi is the man of works, whose efforts are largely concerned with the cause and effect of worldly affairs, relating these to their spiritual equivalents. The Raja Yogi aims at achieving Union through austerities and mental powers, but the Bhakti's sole aim is Union with the Divine through devotion and service, living with thoughts of the Divine ever before him, imagining the Divine as dwelling in the heart.

The Gita expresses these sentiments as follows:

"Of these (devotees) the knower who is ever in Union with the Divine, whose devotion to Me is single-minded, he is the best for he loves me with perfection and is beloved by Me (7–17).

"Noble are all these (devotees), but the knower is in truth Myself, for he is in Union with Me, the Purushotama, his highest goal (7–18)."

In verse (12–1) Arjuna asks: "Those devotees who worship thee steadfastly, and those who worship the Immutable, which of these is better."

Krishna replies:

"Those who concentrate their minds upon Me, steadfastly and with supreme faith, those I consider to be in perfect Union (12–2).

"But those who worship the Immutable, the Unmanifest, the

Eternal, with all senses controlled and undisturbed under all conditions, giving thought to the welfare of all creatures, they also come to Me (12–3–4).

"But the path of those who worship the Immutable, Unmanifest is more difficult, for the Unmanifest is hard to reach by embodied beings (12–5).

"The Yogi is greater than the man of knowledge and greater than the man of words; become thou the Yogi (6–46).

"Of all the Yogis, that one with his inner self given up in sacrifice to Me, him I consider to be the most united to Me, because for Me he has love and faith (6–47).

"The Supreme, in whom abide all creatures and who Pervades all, can be gained by unswerving devotion (8–22)."

The following advice is then given:

"Hear thou my Supreme Word, the highest of all, because thou art beloved of Me I shall tell what is good for thee (18–64).

"Whatever action thou perform, whatever food thou eat, whatever thou offer in sacrifice, whatever thou give in charity, whatever austerity thou practise, do thou make it an offering to Me (9–27).

"So, thou shalt be freed from good and evil which are the bonds of action. So, with the heart steadfast in renunciation, and so liberated, thou shalt come to Me (9–28).

"I do not differentiate among beings, all are the same to Me. None are hateful and none are dear to Me. But those who worship Me with devotion, they dwell in Me and I in them (9–29).

"Fix thy mind upon Me, become my devotee, give sacrifice to Me and give Me reverence. So, having made the heart steadfast upon Me, knowing Me to be the highest goal, so shalt thou come to me.

"By steadfast devotion to Me I may be perceived, I may be known and seen in Reality and may be joined in Union (11–54).

"He who offers all his works for Me alone, he who has Me alone for his goal, he who is free from attachments and is devoted to Me, he who has no enemy amonst all creatures, he enters into Me (11–55).

"If thou art united with Me at all times in heart and mind, then by My Grace thou shalt overcome all obstacles. But if thine ears are closed by self-esteem, then thou shalt be cast aside (18–58).

"If thou take refuge in Him and dedicate thy whole self to Him, then by His Grace thou shalt obtain supreme peace and Heaven (18–62).

"Fill thy mind with Me, be devoted to Me, offer sacrifice to Me and bow down before Me. So, I promise thou shalt come to Me for I love thee dearly (18–65)."

In one verse of the Gita, Krishna clearly indicates that God is aware of our wants and needs, and furthermore that He will fill the needs of His devotees:

"Those in whose mind I am the sole object of thought, those worshipping Me and in constant Union with Me, to them I give that which they have not, and preserve the things they already have (9–22)."

It is also taught in the same chapter, that the sinful are not cast out, but by turning aside from sin and becoming devotees, they also can attain the Highest:

"Even a man of evil, turning to Me with sole and perfect love, must be regarded as righteous, for he has rightly determined (9–30).

"Swiftly he becomes a soul of righteousness and attains eternal peace. No devotee of Mine will ever perish (9–31).

"Even those of inferior birth, taking refuge in Me will attain the highest goal (9–32)."

The Christian religion teaches that it is of the greatest importance to hold Christ in mind at the time of death, and special rites are performed on the dying (such as "Extreme Unction") to ensure their "state of Grace" at that time.

Chapter 8 of the Gita is clearly in agreement, where Krishna says:

"Whoever leaves the body at time of death, with Me alone in mind, comes to My state of being without doubt (8–5).

"Therefore at all times remember Me, for if thy mind and Buddhi are always centred on Me and sacrificed to Me, then to Me thou shalt surely come (8–7).

"He who meditates upon Me, beyond the darkness of ignorance, at the time of death, full of devotion, with mind steadfast by the power of Yoga, fixing the whole life-energy between the eyebrows, he attains to the Supreme (8–9/10).

"With all senses controlled, with the mind concentrated upon the heart, drawing the life-energy upwards into the head and uttering My Name as he leaves the body, he goes to higher worlds (8–12/13).

"Those who, in old age, take refuge in Me, knowing Me in all My forms, they sustain knowledge of Me even at death so attain the Highest (7–29/30)."

Raja Yoga

This is really the province of Patanjali, whose "Yoga Sutras" deal exclusively with Raja Yoga.

This school of Yoga will therefore be dealt with more fully in the chapter devoted to Patanjali, but the general principles of Raja may be expressed as follows.

Raja Yoga – sometimes called the Royal Yoga, or the Yoga of the Mind – is highly regarded as a complete system in itself, by which one can be trained to a state in which the Personal Divine can be perceived, and its union with the Cosmic Divine achieved.

It is essentially concerned with mental functions, using the mind to analyse one's own biological functions, the life forces which operate them and the principles behind them.

The life-force in every being and every created thing is Prana, the "absolute" energy of the universe from which all other forms of energy are derived. The subtle forces of the spiritual world, electrical energy, magnetism, heat, light and the force of sound waves, are all derived from this Primary Energy.

Through the practices of mental concentration, meditation and contemplation, the mind is directed inwards to investigate the flow of Prana Energy through the body. Nerve currents, thought energy, the dynamic energy which drives the bodily organs and muscles – all of those are energised by the Pranic flow.

In following the operation of Prana in the body, those laws by which it operates can be apprehended. Those same laws apply through all creation, so that we can then learn to apply them to all created things. More important, however, is the fact that, having learnt to control Prana in our own body, and having learnt to control it in the functions of nature, a point is reached where the Purusha itself is apprehended and this is the real true goal of Raja Yoga.

In order to perceive the Purusha, it is necessary to still the mind, and the simile is drawn, showing the mind as a pond whose surface is broken up by the ripples of thought, so that the Purusha, dwelling in the depths of the pond cannot be seen for the agitation on the broken surface.

If, however, the surface of the pond is controlled to a point of perfect stillness, then the bottom can be seen, or the Purusha can be perceived.

Raja Yoga therefore begins by teaching mental concentration and mind control, as a preliminary to holding the mind still, perfectly free from the disturbance of thought, and detached from all sense perceptions.

It is always emphasised that the first essential in Raja Yoga is the attainment of a high standard of morality and physical fitness. If the mind is impure, or our purposes are directed to worldly gains, then our efforts will fail and may bring disaster in their train. If we are physically unfit, then the forces which are generated in the practices and exercises could be physically harmful and mentally damaging.

To this end, specific instructions are given regarding behaviour, morals and training, and these will be dealt with in the following chapter. As in this chapter we are concerned principally with the teaching of the Gita, the following extracts from the chapters of the Gita clearly indicate the teaching and the training necessary.

"Those who are released from desire and passion, who have gained self mastery and self knowledge (by the practice of Raja Yoga) achieve Nirvana (5–26).

"Closing the mind to all external objects, with vision fixed between the eyebrows and with even regular breath, with senses, mind and Buddhi controlled and liberation as the supreme goal, being freed from desire, passion and fear, one is indeed free for eternity (5–27/28).

"Remaining alone and in solitude, self controlled and freed from all desires, let the Yogi constantly concentrate his mind (6–10).

"Firmly seated in a place which is clean, neither too high nor too low, and covered with a cloth over which is placed a deerskin (let the Yogi meditate) (6–11).

"Seated there with mind concentrated, controlling thoughts and senses, practise Yoga for self purification (6–12).

"With body, head and neck held steady (in a straight line) with gaze fixed firmly at the tip of the nose (let the Yogi meditate) (6–13).

"Serene and fearless, firm in celibacy, with mind controlled and thoughts concentrated upon Me, let him meditate, having Me as his Supreme goal (6–14).

"Keeping the mind thus steady and subdued, the Yogi attains to peace, dwelling with me in Nirvana (6–15).

"This Yoga is not for him who eats too much or sleeps too much, nor for him who gives up sleep and food (practising too much austerity) (6–16).

"For he whose habits of eating and recreation are temperate, whose actions are restrained, whose sleeping and working are regulated, for him Yoga is the destroyer of misery (6–17).

"When consciousness is completely controlled and is concentrated in the Self alone, free from all desires and passions he is said to be in Yoga (Union) (6–18).

"Even as a lamp flickers not in a windless place so is a Yogi of controlled mind, practising Union with the Self (6–19).

"That in which the mind is silent and stilled by Yoga, that in which the Self beholds the Self and rejoices in the Self, that in which the Self knows its own truth and ecstasy, that which Buddhi perceives and is beyond the senses, that in which, once established he no longer falls from the truth of its being, that on gaining which he perceives there is no greater goal, that in which, once established he is not moved by pain or senses. Let that be known as Yoga which is to be practised with determination and perseverance (6–20/23).

"Peace is won gradually by means of Buddhi (intellect) with the mind controlled and fixed upon the Self. Think then of nothing else (6–25).

"When the wavering minds drift away (from the point of meditation) bring it back to be centred upon the Self alone (6–26).

"When the mind is stilled without thought or passion, there enters the highest bliss of the Soul in its Unity with Brahman (6–27).

"Whose self is in Yoga, sees the Self in all creation and all creation in the Self (6–29).

"With all doors to the senses closed and mind concentrated upon the heart, drawing Prana into the head and reciting the sacred syllable 'OM' he who then leaves the body attains to Divine Status (8–12/13).

"Uniting the purified mind (with Purusha) persevering with control of the body and the senses, abstaining from sensual delights, living in solitude, eating little, meditating always, forsaking passion, egoism, pride, power, lust and property, with tranquil mind he becomes One with Brahman (18–51/53)."

Karma Yoga

The full implications of Karma Yoga are not always fully understood, and much misrepresentation has resulted.

Karma is frequently equated with blind Fate, in which the individual has little or no control over the circumstances of his life, but is driven willy-nilly by a faceless force. This is given the name of "Fate", especially when circumstances prove to be adverse.

In fact Karma is a law as precise and unchaging as the Law of Gravity and the Laws which govern electricity and magnetism.

Stated in its most elementary form, one may say that Karma is the Law of Cause and Effect, and referring again to electricity and magnetism, their Law states that 1 volt of electrical pressure is generated when 1 million lines of magnetic force are cut by a loop of wire in 1 second – no more and no less, the Law is precise, and the whole of our electrical power generation is based upon this simple fact.

A magnetic field can exist for all eternity, but no electricity will be generated until action is taken to cut those lines of force with a closed conductor. The resulting effect we know, the cause is the basic phenomenon of the field and the *action* which is necessary to achieve the resulting electrical energy.

The basic Physical Laws hold good throughout the world, regardless of where or when they are operated, or by whom. The Law of Karma is as precise and unchangeable, and it is essential to every man's happiness and peace of mind to know the Law and to know how it may be applied to his (or her) advantage.

The first fact to recognise is that Right action causes effects which are beneficial whereas wrong action can only operate to our ultimate disadvantage.

In some religions this sequence of cause and effect has been translated into terms of reward and punishment, but this is an over-simplification which leads to misunderstanding of the facts. If a small boy steals a green apple and eats it, he will most certainly suffer for his wrong action, and his father may well point out that this is a "punishment" for his "sin". But the fact is that even before he stole the apple, the boy had set in motion a train of events which resulted in the inevitable effect of suffering.

The primary cause of his final discomfort was *desire*, a desire for the apple, which was then converted into the act of stealing, the act of eating, and the chemical reaction which resulted in pain.

The primary cause was therefore a *mental* activity.

The Law of Karma must be seen in the same light, for all action is preceded by a mental idea, so that if we learn to control our ideas, then we have learnt to control our actions, and have taken a great step forward on the "Path of Attainment", the path to happiness and peace.

Patanjali states quite clearly that "Yoga is control of ideas in the mind". Its purpose is not only to ensure peace and happiness, but also to attain liberation from bondage to earthly attachments and desires, and so from pain and suffering. Yoga also teaches that we are thereby liberated from the cycle of births and deaths which attachments and desires bring inevitably in their train.

In order to appreciate that this is not simply a "rule" thought up by ascetics to make life more difficult, the mechanism by which the Law operates should be closely studied.

Whenever a thought passes through the mind, or an action takes place, an impression (called a Sanskara) is made upon the mind-stuff (called Chitta). These impressions form a sort of path to which other thoughts of a similar kind are attracted and through which they flow in a continuing process, by which habits are formed.

The process has been likened to a piece of string being wound, or unwound, on a pencil. When a thought or action takes place, a loop of string is wound around the pencil, and the more frequently this happens, the greater becomes the desire, or the more firmly fixed is the habit.

Conversely, if it is desired to break the habit, then a coil is unwound or removed, by strong thought in opposition to the original, or by denying the desire when it arises (see also *Yoga the Key to Life*), or by "retribution" and penance.

It must therefore be seen that we are truly the masters of our own destiny for by a proper "control of ideas in the mind" we are able to create conditions which are favourable rather than adverse, we can be the person we wish to be, and can live in peace.

Karmic Law, therefore, operates through the physical and
mental planes to the spiritual, so that our future, even in
eternity, is decided by ourselves in the "here and now". Who,
knowing this, could follow any but the "Righteous Path"?

The Gita teaches that there is a particular state of mind which
leads to right action and it is called "Naish-Karma". Actions
carried out in this state of mind leave no impression, and
Sanskaras do not occur, so there are no consequent "effects".

Normally, impressions left upon the soul by Sanskaras are the
cause of further actions in an endless round of cause and effect,
but this process is halted by Naish-Karma. The methods by
which this can be achieved are taught in the Gita.

"He whose mind is controlled with perfect detachment,
whose Self is controlled, and whose desires have been
conquered, he attains by renunciation the supreme perfection
of Naish-Karma (18–49)."

In the earlier chapters also we find references to the
conditions by which Naish-Karma are achieved:

"Dedicating all thy actions to Me, with thy consciousness
fixed in thy Self, free from all desire, attachment and eogism, do
thy duty (3–30)."

"Having abandoned attachments and being steadfast in
Yoga, perform all actions. Yoga brings equality of distinctions
between success and failure which is evenness of mind (2–48)."

The Gita also makes the point that inaction does not lead to
Naish-Karma. This is a clear warning against the lazy man's
interpretation of Karmic Law, when he allows himself to believe
that Nirvana can be attained by personal detachment from
work.

"Not by abstention from works is Naish-Karma attained, nor
can perfection be achieved by renunciation alone (3–4).

"No man can exist for a moment without doing work. The
Gunas of Prakriti compel everyone to action. If a man restrains
his action but continues to allow his mind to brood on the
objects of sense, he is a hypocrite. Perform, then, thy allotted
work, knowing that action is better than inaction, for even to
maintain life in the body, work must be done and actions carried
out (3–5/6/8).

". . . let there not be attachment to inactivity (2–47)."

There is frequently a difficulty in deciding whether an action
is "right" or "wrong", for those are relative terms.

Yoga teaches that no action is either completely right or completely wrong, that each contains an element of the other.

In its simplest form one can point to a man who steals money or food to provide for a starving family. From the family's point of view the action could be considered "right" but from the owner's point of view and from the legal point of view, the act would be criminal and therefore judged as "wrong".

The Gita accepts the difficulty of discrimination and Arjuna asks guidance from the Lord Krishna, who replies:

"As to what is action and what is inaction, even the wise are bewildered. I will declare to thee what is action, and knowing this thou shalt be saved from doing evil (4–16).

"One must understand what is action and what is wrong action and what is inaction. Thick and tangled is the way of Works (4–17).

"He who sees inaction in action and action in inaction, he has wisdom (4–18).

"He whose mind is unclouded by desire, whose works are consumed in the fire of Knowledge, the wise men call a Sage (4–19).

"Abandoning all attachment to the fruits of action, even content and independent, in doing nothing, he yet engages in action (4–20).

"Free from desires, fully self-controlled, giving up all possession, performing those actions required by the body alone, he commits no wong (4–21).

"He who accepts whatever comes with equanimity, who has passed beyond the duality of opposites, who is without jealousy, undisturbed by failure or success, his acts do not bind him (4–22).

"For the Sage who desires to reach the Highest in Yoga, Karma is the way. When he has attained the Highest in Yoga all action is Serene (6–3).

"Where there is no attachment either to the objects of sense or to the fruits of work, and when all desires have been subdued, that man has reached the Highest in Yoga (6–4).

"Those without knowledge speak of asceticism and the performing of works as difficult things, but not so the wise, for he who applies himself diligently to the one obtains the fruits of both (5–5)."

Arjuna is puzzled by the apparent contradiction whereby

renunciation of works is taught by Krishna and at the same time performance of works as the Way to Attainment.

Arjuna asks:

"You have taught me that renunciation of works is the right way, but you have also taught that performance of works brings liberation, which is the better way, which is right? (5-1).

"Krishna said: Both the renunciation of works and their performance bring salvation (i.e. works performed with a knowledge of their Karma). But Karma Yoga is better than renunciation of works (5-2).

"He who is trained in Karma Yoga, is pure in spirit and has attained Self-mastery, who has control of his senses and whose Self is absorbed in the Self of all existences, even though he performs works, he is detached from them (5-7).

"Without Karma Yoga, renunciation is difficult to attain. He who is trained in Karma Yoga soon attains the Highest (5-6).

"He who carries out his duties without regard for the fruits thereof, he is the only one, not he who neither lights the sacrificial fire or does the work (6-1).

"The three gunas of action, pleasant, unpleasant and mixed, which accrue in this or other worlds, these are for the slaves of desire and ego. These things do not cling to those who have renounced (18-12).

"Arjuna said: Tell me the principles of Sannyas and of Tyag (renunciation) (18-1).

"Krishna replied: Some say that all actions should be given up as evil, whilst others say that acts of sacrifice, penance and charity should not be given up. Hear the truth from Me about Tyag which has been explained as threefold.

"Acts of sacrifice, penance and charity should not be given up for their performance purifies the wise, but even these actions must be performed without regard for the fruits thereof.

"Renunciation of rightly controlled actions is not proper. Renunciation in ignorance is Tamasic.

"He who renounces work from fear of pain or suffering, loses the rewards of renunciation, for this is Rajasic.

"He who performs actions because they are necessary, without attachment to either the doing of the action or the fruits thereof is rewarded, as that is regarded as Satvic.

"The wise man whose mind is fully Satvic and without doubts, has no aversion to unpleasant tasks, and has no attachment to pleasant tasks (18–3/10)."

The Gita clearly places emphasis upon discrimination. Man must work in order to live, but he must ensure that the fruits of his work are completely free from taint of any sort. Otherwise a chain of events may be started which could result in injury. Thus the seeds of "bad Karma" would be sown, which must inevitably react adversely upon the originator.

Outstanding examples may be found even in recent history. Hitler and Mussolini, both men of special powers and talents, allowed themselves to be diverted into wrong channels and actions. Lust for power, perverted nationalism, egoism and greed, brought about their downfall with chaos and suffering to the world.

Karma Yoga deals with works and the fruits thereof, but as we know, a preliminary state exists in the mind prior to an action taking place, and it is at this point that control really begins.

This is the sphere of Raja Yoga, which we will deal with in our next chapter.

CHAPTER 5

Patanjali and The Yoga Sutras

It is almost incredible that the man who is known as the "Father of Yoga" is himself unknown, but the truth is that nothing certain is known of the man himself, or even the date of his existence. Opinions differ on the latter point, but it is now accepted generally that Patanjali lived during the period 300–200 B.C. and his Aphorisms are dated accordingly.

Although he is called the Father of Yoga, Patanjali did not invent Yoga, but with profound insight and clarity he assembled what knowledge and experience was available at that time, added to this his own knowledge and experience, and formed from these a system of instruction which has remained a classic of its kind.

The aphorisms are brief to the point of obscurity, and in reading them, one has the impression that they are a series of abbreviated notes, written more as a memorandum giving principal guidelines, than as a textbook for instructional purposes. Certainly they are useless to beginners as they stand.

However this may be, the Aphorisms are of the greatest value in setting out with a remarkable economy of words, a course of instruction in Yoga, It is, however, a particular branch of Yoga, which deals with mental control and the psychic powers developed thereby. It is the School which is called Raja Yoga.

Because of the extreme brevity of the aphorisms and the fact that they were originally written in Sanskrit, both translation and interpretation have been both necessary and difficult, and following literal translations from the Sanskrit, commentaries have been written by numbers of people in an attempt at elucidation and interpretation.

Paul Brunson in his Introduction to Professor Wood's book, writes: ". . . only those who know from actual experience what they read about in the text, can really understand Patanjali . . . because, whereas others have sought truth by intellectual logic,

Patanjali sought it by intellect-transcending meditation . . . his writings were primarily intended for the use of teachers rather than for the use of students. They were really a series of subject headings of which explanations could be given personally and lectures could be delivered vocally. . . . Hence a modern commentary is necessary."

As we have already noted the Yoga system of Patanjali is now one of the Six Classical Systems of Indian Philosophy.

In both the history and practice of Yoga, the Aphorisms play a vital part, for whereas up to the time of Patanjali teaching depended largely upon the ability and experience of the teacher, his own personal interpretation of the Vedas and Upanishads, and his own personal skill in putting this over, verbally, to his students, Patanjali laid down specific instructions which, once they were understood, formed a concise and detailed system by which the aims of Yoga could be achieved.

As we have said, this system is known as Raja Yoga, and it is specifically concerned with training mind and will in concentration, meditation and contemplation, in which that which is contemplated is the Real Self. The state finally attained is blissful Union with the Divine which is the state of true Samadhi and the true goal of Yoga.

This is the state to which the Vedas, the Upanishads and the Gita point unanimously as being the Highest Goal.

Patanjali has divided the aphorisms into four groups or sections, but the sections do not begin with the simplest, introductory aphorisms as one would expect.

Section 1 deals with Contemplation.
Section 2 deals with Practices.
Section 3 deals with Psychic Powers.
Section 4 deals with Independence.
Let us examine these in the order as laid down by Patanjali:

Section I – Contemplation

We are at once thrown in at the deep end, for Aphorism 1 says "Now – instruction in Yoga": Our attention is immediately riveted and our mind orientated to the subject. The teacher has established rapport with his students. Aphorism 2 says that "Yoga is the control of ideas in the mind." What a world of philosophy there is in this brief statement, for whole books have been written on that subject alone. But the student must bring to this, as to the rest of the aphorisms, a considerable amount of prior knowledge and experience before the full impact of the statement becomes clear.

We have already said that all action is preceded by an idea in the mind, for until the mind has pictured the action, the necessary nervous reaction cannot be triggered off. Without mental activity there can be no physical activity. This, we have seen in our brief study of Karma.

In the sense of Raja Yoga, however, Buddhi is brought into play in order that our thoughts and ideas may be assessed and discriminated. This must be done dispassionately with a scientific marshalling of fact, of cause and effect, so that an attitude of detachment must be cultivated or our assessment will be "coloured" and biased by habit and desire.

Once we are able to control our thoughts (or "ideas in the mind") we are also able to establish self-control, on the basis that thought precedes action.

Also, we are then in a position to direct what sort of ideas the mind will attract and consider, so we thereby become orientated away from the material to the spiritual, where lies one's true happiness. As St. Paul puts it, we then "walk in the Spirit".

It is clearly established at the outset, then, that our first task is a mental examination, an assessment of our thoughts and ideals followed by the establishment of thought control.

Aphorism 3 states "Then there is dwelling of the Looker in his own proper nature."

The "Looker" is of course ourself, and we know that we are, in our "proper nature" Spirit. Patanjali is therefore telling us that when we have established a proper mental control, and have reached a degree where all ideas in the mind can be stilled, and our consciousness can then move into a phase of transcendence, when the Real Self can be contemplated. We are then truly "in the Spirit".

"Otherwise," says Aphorism 4, "there is identification with the ideas."

If the mind remains uncontrolled, and our thoughts are allowed free rein, they are inevitably attracted to the things of the senses, to circumstance and environment, and there is then no possibility of orientation to the spirit, and the achievement of that super-conscious state which is the goal of Raja Yoga.

It is well worth pausing for a moment to consider the effect of ideas upon our daily life. Indeed, it is true to say that our daily life is controlled almost entirely by our ideas. If we apply this statement in reverse, it is also true that if we can control our ideas, we can also establish a large measure of control over our daily life and our future.

For example, man is by nature a creature of habit, and if we trace the chain of events which led up to those habits, we will find that, as in all things, they answer to the laws of cause and effect.

In the first place we must have been attracted to something which appeared pleasing to us or which we thought necessary in order to conform with social custom (e.g. smoking!). This attraction would appear as an image in the mind which, consciously or otherwise, we would imagine ourselves experiencing. A desire is then created, and the necessary action is taken to satisfy that desire.

The idea has now been transformed into action.

If the action is repeated, the desire is strengthened, so that a habit is formed and eventually we find ourselves the slave of the habit (e.g. a man takes a drink then the drink takes a drink, then drink takes the man).

It can be seen that had we assessed the "idea in the mind" when it first arose, and discriminated on whether it was beneficial or otherwise, whether we were prepared to accept its continuation or not, we would have been able to control our subsequent actions or even to deny their taking place.

This fundamental process is of the greatest importance, and it is recommended that the student examine it closely and then relate this to his own daily habits, and to assess by how much he (or she) would rate as an automaton, responding automatically to circumstance and environment in an entirely predictable manner, and without conscious thought.

Until it is appreciated that this is so, very little progress will be made in the practice of mental control, for one must be aware of a thing before one can control it.

The insidious process of modern advertising is based upon the injection of ideas into the mind. The product being advertised is almost invariably associated with something which gives pleasure, even though that something has no real association with the product. The intention is to create a desire which (according to the advertisement) the product will satisfy.

Our first ideas are created from experiences in the cradle when we learn that certain actions bring certain results. We learn how to attract attention and to express elementary needs. At school, ideas of "fair play" and ideologies are inculcated and we learn to what sort of behaviour we must conform in order to be acceptable to the community in which we live.

These ideas form the basis of future concepts. They colour our thoughts and actions in later life. In other words patterns of thought and behaviour are impressed upon the mind which, in the general case, ensures compatibility with the rest of the community.

But most of such is effective only in the material sense, and is designed to establish and maintain law-and-order and conformity. We can live as automatons within this framework, or we can expand our intellect and our consciousness, even into transcendence, in which a knowledge of super-sensible states can be realised.

If we are content to live as a "standard product" of our race and time, bound up with the rat-race of promotions and status symbols, then we shall probably either die prematurely of heart failure or a stroke, or reach old age in a state of bewildered disappointment, wondering what it has all been about.

If, on the other hand, we accept our spiritual nature, learn the language of the spirit, and allow our consciousness to transcend the mundane, then, on the Path of Attainment we shall find true peace and joy, secure in faith, knowledge and the future.

The process by which the knowledge is obtained and our faith established is Yoga, and Raja Yoga is the means of mental control which leads to transcendent knowledge.

"Otherwise," warns Patanjali, "there is identification with the ideas" (1–4), and we shall never progress beyond the stage of automatic reaction to established ideas and concepts.

Aphorism 5 states "There are five kinds of ideas, painful and pleasant," whilst Aphorism 6 tells us that these are "Right knowledge, wrong knowledge, fancy, sleep and memories."

Much has been said and written as to what constitutes "right knowledge" and "wrong knowledge". Clearly the first definition must be that right knowledge is beneficial and is therefore "right" from the points of view of harmony, health, and progress. Conversely, "wrong" knowledge must be that which is erroneous, misleading, based on false information or premise, and must therefore be harmful and antagonistic to progress.

One has to take care, also, of the definition of "knowledge", for to *know* a thing is to have experienced it, which is quite a different thing to *belief*. Right knowledge and wrong knowledge therefore point to the need for discrimination as to what experiences and theories we investigate. We must be sure that they are Satvic and not Tamasic, or we shall progress in a wrong direction.

Patanjali lists Right Knowledge as "perception, inferences and testimonies", and Wrong Knowledge as "false knowledge, fixed in a form not according to a thing".

Professor Wood points out that, with regard to perception, inferences and testimonies, these constitute three ways of obtaining ideas. The first is through sensory perception, the second as when we infer one thing from another (e.g. all men have brains so that Mr. X, being a man, must have a brain). As to testimony, we must ensure that an informant is reliable, and himself correctly informed.

Wrong knowledge can also be obtained by "perception, inference and testimonies", but the reference to form places the emphasis on "perception". Most people will have read the story of the soldier who, whilst in India and preparing for bed one night, sees two round bright objects staring from under the bed. Transfixed by the hypnotic stare of what he takes to be a snake, the man spends the night with his attention riveted to those two eyes. He is found exhausted the next morning, whilst under the bed was found a leather belt whose buckle was adorned with two glass beads.

Similarly, in the dark, the shapes of furniture and hanging clothes can take on a personality different to their own, and Patanjali tells us we must look beyond the form immediately apparent, to the true nature behind the form in order to draw the right conclusions. Aphorism 9 says that "Fancy is settling upon word-knowledge, there being no such thing" (as the Flying Horse of Arabian Nights and in fairy tales). Aphorism 10 "Sleep is the idea based upon the conception of absence": Sleep is produced when consciousness is absent, but inasmuch as the mind is still active in sleep, it still produces ideas.

Aphorism 11 "Memory is the non-loss of objects in knowledge." In activating memory, one brings before the mind the object of memory and the experiences associated with the object. This also works in reverse, as when one experiences a scent or a sound, the memory is evoked of circumstances in which this has been experienced previously, the occasion or event is then remembered.

In Aphorisms 5–11, therefore, Patanjali outlines the five classifications of ideas. The importance of this is that before we can control a thing we must come to recognise or identify it, and as our lives are more or less governed by our ideas, we must learn to discriminate as to their classification, to make a decision as to whether they may be harmful or beneficial, and to either still them at birth or encourage them by meditation.

Aphorism 12 states "Control of ideas is established by practice and uncolouredness."

It is self-evident that without frequent practice there could be no control, but it is important to realise that practice must be applied at all times. Occasionally, in our daily work and leisure, it is helpful to stop, momentarily, and assess the ideas which are currently passing through the mind, to pull oneself up at times and watch the trend of thought.

This can be very revealing as to our own true personality, but also serves as a first step to mental control.*

Aphorisms 13 and 14 state "Practice is the effort towards steadiness, which becomes firmly grounded by devotion, uninterrupted over a long period."

As to "uncolouredness", it is equally clear that, in order to give the right judgement, we must approach our examination with detachment so that we may remain unbiased. If we allow preconceptions to dictate our answers, we may only fall further into error and further away from truth.

Aphorism 15 says "Uncolouredness is the consciousness of power of one who is free from desire for objects seen or heard of." In other words, one is detached.

Aphorism 16 "It is higher where there is no desire for the Qualities of Nature due to knowledge about the Real Man."

The Qualities of Nature are, of course, the Gunas already referred to, which appear in varying quantity in all of nature. When once we have accepted our spiritual birthright and no longer regard the physical man as the true "I am", then the desires for sensual experience which are natural to the purely

* See also *Yoga the Key to Life* for detailed description.

physical man, are tempered and refined through the eyes of the spirit. Habits which are normal and desirable to the "animal" are abhorrent to the spirit.

In this state, the mind, with clear sight and purified motives will have reached a high stage of "uncolouredness" leading to right judgement, perspicuity and perspicacity.

The three "Qualities" or Gunas (Satva, Rajas and Tamas) exist not only in the physical, but also in the mental and spiritual spheres, and Professor Wood points out that in Yogi Philosophy these are the "ultimates out of which all objective forms are made by compounding in different proportions".

He then described the Qualities as referring to "matter, energy and natural law, being (a) law, harmony, order, rhythm, purity (Satvic), (b) motion, activity, restlessness (Rajasic), (c) materiality, resistivity, inertia, dullness, darkness (Tamasic)."

Aphorisms 17–18 state: "Contemplation brings knowledge when accompanied by forms, meditation, joy or a sense of power. When the mental image of stoppage is practised old habit-moulds tend to re-assess."

Aphorisms 19–20 state: "In those beings in the bodiless state and those whose minds are absorbed in contemplation of Nature, there is still the thought of existence" (i.e. they still have the "I am" consciousness). In the case of others it is preceded by faith, vigour, memory, contemplation and understanding.

Aphorisms 21–23 can be read as "For those whose impetus (of concentration and spiritual desire) is intense, Samadhi is near, but even this state has distinctions of the Qualities. Devotion to God will bring on this state."

Aphorisms 24–29 state: "God is a particular being, unaffected by Qualities and Karma. He is the supreme source of all knowledge. He is eternal and was teacher of the ancient (as well as man today). He is known by the Sacred Word (OM), which shall be repeated with meditation upon its meanings. From such meditation comes understanding and absence of obstacles."

From Aphorisms 30–34 we learn: "Disease, dullness, sloth, indecision, carelessness, materialism, wrong views and instability are obstacles to Contemplation, as also are distress, despair, nervousness and irregular breathing. Practice of Yoga overcomes these, whilst purity of mind comes with habits of friendliness, sympathy, joy and equanimity. By proper breath control (Pranayama) obstacles can also be overcome." (See *Yoga the Key to Life*.)

Aphorisms 35–40 state: "The mind is steadied by developing sensitivity, the peaceful Inner-Light, and freedom from desires. Also dwelling upon knowledge of dream and sleep and from the practice of meditation. Mastery (of mind) extends from the smallest of things to the greatest."

In Aphorisms 41–43 we are told, "Correct imagery is the reception of those things which can be related to the knower, to knowing or to what is known, when the ideas relating to them have faded and the mind is absorbed as with gazing upon a flawless gem. Correct imagery, called inspectional, is when there is meditation upon the meanings of words and knowledge.

"When ideas are stilled and the mind shines forth on the object alone as though it had discarded its own nature, and become the object, it has become non-inspectional."

Aphorisms 44–45 then say: "The same explanation applies to those meditations which have the subtle for their objective. Such objectiveness cannot go beyond to that which cannot be defined."

Aphorisms 46–51: "The preceding are described as Contemplation with seed, but when skill has been achieved in non-inspectional Contemplation, the Self is revealed, when there is cognition of full truth. Such cognition differs from that obtained by inference and testimony as it deals with particulars, and the habit-mould developed by practice of such meditation destroys all previous habit-moulds.

"When even the higher habit-mould is controlled seedless Contemplation arrives and there is control of all."

Section II – Practice

In a course of instruction, it would appear more reasonable to allow Section II to precede Section I, for the latter is not only more simple than Section II, but also gives the preliminary exercises without which Section II cannot reasonably be approached.

For example, Aphorism II/1 states that "Yoga in active life consists of Body-Conditioning, Self-study, and Attentiveness to God."

If this sentence is taken to its ultimate conclusion, it is realized that all the principal schools of Yoga are introduced with these few words. The reference to "active life" would refer to those taking the "Path of Works", in other words – Karma Yoga. Body-conditioning we know as Hatha Yoga, Self-study we meet in both Raja and Jnana Yoga, whilst "Attentiveness to God" points to the way of Love and Devotion which is Bhakta Yoga.

In one short sentence therefore, Patanjali has indicated that a study of nothing less than the "whole man" is necessary if we wish to advance. A fit body will not help us alone; a properly informed and trained mind is also necessary. Conversely, it is held that, due to psychosomatic relationships, it is not possible to have a mind completely detached, objective, controlled and needle-sharp, if it is carried in an ailing body which is constantly clamouring for attention.

"Know thyself" has been the command of every religious leader. Buddha and Jesus both emphasised that before we look to know anything else, we must first look within. Patanjali's expression "Self-study", directs us to aim at the Real Self, not merely the physical or mental, for these are but stepping stones to the true Reality.

Attentiveness to God must be in our heart and mind at all times and under all circumstances, whether at work or play, or our efforts will be led into materialism and a desire for rewards. We would then be chained by those very things which should lead us to liberation, and the seers have at all times warned against allowing ourselves to be diverted into byways which may be fascinating in themselves, but which fail to lead us onwards. A true love of God puts all things into proper perspective.

In Aphorism II/2 Patanjali tells us that the Three Practices have "the purpose of promoting Contemplation and reducing the Sources of Trouble".

The latter, Patanjali says, are "Ignorance, Self-love, desires, aversions, possessiveness" (Aphorism II/3). He then proceeds to define them in Aphorisms II–4–9 as follows:

"Ignorance is the ground which nurtures all the others, whether they are dormant, slight, obstructive or vigorous (4).

"Ignorance is in regarding that which is temporal (non-eternal), impure, painful and not self, as eternal pure, pleasant and Self (5).

"Self-love is the unification of the looker and the organs of looking (6).

"Desire is a follower of pleasure (7) (i.e. is the result of).

"Aversion is a follower of pain (8) (i.e. is the result of).

"Possessiveness, which is firmly rooted, even in the learned, is encouraged by its own delights (9)."

Aphorism II/10 states, "The sources of trouble when subtle (i.e. mental ideas only) may be removed by the generation of their opposite," whilst II/11 says "Their forms (i.e. active expression) are removable by meditation."

The next Aphorisms II/12–14 require some explanation. They state, "The Karma container has its roots in the sources of trouble and is experienced in the spheres of the seen and unseen (12). Once rooted, it ripens to life-condition, length of life and experience (13). These bear fruit in joy and grief which are caused by virtue and vice respectively (14)."

The "Karma-container" is the whole man, that is, it consists not only of the physical body, but the psychic and ethereal, in fact all these parts, subtle and physical which are the receptacles of Sanskaras, from which are derived Karmas, both past and present, whose fruits are currently being worked out or which have yet to come.

What thoughts and actions have already been accomplished, will have sown the seeds of future Karma, and they may even be working out in the present, If, as Patanjali says, our actions have been virtuous, then we will experience their Karma as joy, but if, on the other hand, we have inflicted pain on others, or have caused suffering to others in any shape or form, then the fruit of such action is worked out in our own Karma as an experience of grief.

Therefore, Patanjali tells us plainly that we cannot divorce one part from another, for man is inter-related and co-ordinated in all his parts, so that thoughts work themselves out as actions and both thought and action create that which is called Karma, and this affects our experiences and circumstances throughout our lifetime, even into the next world.

A simple example of the psychosomatic relationship is that of the worried businessman, who generates such turmoil in himself that ulcers or high blood pressure are the result. In other words, an attitude of mind is reflected in a physical condition, and vice versa.

Aphorism II/15–17 state that "Everything is painful to the discriminating person, because of transformation, worry and habit-mould, and because of obstruction by the formations in the Qualities of Nature (the Gunas) (15). Pain which has not yet come is avoidable (16). The cause of that pain is the conjunction of the Looker with the objects seen (17)."

Aphorism II/15 is complex and difficult to understand. Professor Wood has recognised this as one of the more important aphorisms and has gone to great trouble to give the detailed analysis the aphorism deserves.

The aphorism states that "Everything is painful to the discriminating person, because of transformation, worry, and habit-mould, and because of obstruction by the formations in the Qualities of Nature."

We may summarise an explanation as follows:

All deeds have their karmic effect. If the deed is virtuous, then its effects will be "pleasurable" or beneficial. If, however, the deed is vicious or evil then its effects can only be "painful" or harmful. The Karma thus developed will involve with that already existing, and will be worked out either in the immediate or the distant future, but worked out finally it must be. "As ye sow, so shall ye reap", says the New Testament.

To this, Patanjali adds the observation that "Everything is painful to the discriminating person." It is self-evident that the unthinking, undeveloped person, can go through life almost unaffected by circumstances, events and conditions. He is generally "in-sensitive". A person of developed intellect, however, also has an increased sensitivity, which makes his reactions to external stimuli increasingly stronger. He therefore becomes more and more discriminating in every direction, as to what sounds are acceptable, what colours are acceptable, what environment is bearable, what dress and habits are acceptable and so on.

This increasing sensitivity is a mark of unfolding spiritual consciousness, and is a condition through which all students of Yoga must pass.

Patanjali points to this state of suffering as a mark of development, when he says that this is due to "transformation, worry and habit mould", In transforming ourselves from a run-of-the-mill, unthinking, insensitive individual, to a sensitive, discriminating person, our values will have changed, and habit-moulds (Sanskaras), developed over the years, will now find themselves under the stress of transformation to a new and more sensitive mould.

Therefore, not only do we suffer pain from external sources through our sense perceptions, but we are also under stress from the psycho-physiological changes which take place in our system.

Professor Wood points out that the physical world in which we live, composed as it is of the Three Gunas (or Qualities) in myriad combinations and forms, also proves an obstruction to Yogic ambition and is a further source of pain. Even if we achieve an ambition or fulfil a desire, it is seen to be but a transient, fleeting thing which stays but a little while and is gone, so that even success has its content of pain. This is frequently in the form of worry that we might lose the thing we have gained, so that we must strive to protect it.

In Aphorisms II/16–17 we are told that, "Pain which has not come is avoidable. The cause of that pain is the conjunction of the Looker with the world of objects."

Clearly, if we know the causes of pain, we can take steps to avoid it, and Patanjali has already told us that the "Sources of Trouble" are the cause, and that the "Three Practices" (of Body-Conditioning, Self-study, and Devotion to God) provide the means of overcoming Sources of Trouble.

Also, identifying the physical body as the true Self is confusion born of ignorance, for as we have seen in Aphorism II/6, "Self-personality is the conjunction of the Looker with the instrument of seeing" (i.e. the mind). Professor Wood points out that we therefore have three things to deal with, namely, the Looker, the instrument of seeing, and that which is seen. Patanjali now describes these three in Aphorism, II/18–21.

"The world which is seen consists of all things created and the senses: it exists to give us experience and fulfilment.

"The Qualities of Nature have four divisions; the specialised, the general, the ideal and that which cannot be defined.

"The Looker is consciousness only, which, though pure, sees mental images.

"The essential nature of the seen is for his sake."

The last four statements would at first sight appear vague and almost without meaning, but if we relate them to what we already know, their meaning becomes clear.

"The world which is seen" related to "things created and the senses", clearly refers to the objective (external world) which is composed of the basic elements of earth, air, water, fire, and is experienced through our sense perceptions (the organs of seeing, hearing, etc.). It is compounded of the three Gunas, namely that which is Satvic (illuminating, spiritually luminous), that which is Rajasic (restless, active, moving), and that which is Tamasic (dull, inert, stationary). Vivekananda says* that all nature exists in order that the Purusha may gain experience, to which Wood adds "fulfilment".

Patanjali then continues to categorise the states of the Qualities (or Gunas) which we know as Satvic, Rajasic and Tamasic.

Nature "undefined" is the three Qualities in a state of perfect balance, a state which exists prior to creation, which only "becomes" when imbalance occurs, and a thing is created from the resulting mixtures of the Gunas in varying quantities.

This can be likened to the existence of three forces, all of which are equal in the first place. Acting simultaneously on a point, they would cancel out and then would be no resulting movement, i.e. no action would be created. If any one force changes, however, action and movement would result.

This principle can also be seen as an operation of Karmic Law, creation then being the Karma of movement among the Gunas.

Returning to Aphorism 19, then, we see that Patanjali is putting all of nature into four categories, namely:

1 The specialised – the Self
2 The general or defined – gross elements to which our senses respond
3 The ideal – the area of intellect (Buddhi)
4 The undefined – the state prior to creation.

Aphorism 20 refers to the "Looker" as "consciousness only", which is another way of saying that the Real Self is pure consciousness, which, in spite of its natural purity, is affected by the images passing through the mind, as, for example, a colour is reflected in a mirror. In other words, although the mirror reflects the colour, the mirror itself is in no way modified by the colour, it simply reflects it. So it is with the consciousness, which though it reflects images, is not itself modified by them.

* Raja-Yoga, p. 200.

Patanjali then summarises the purpose of the whole of nature as being created solely for the experience of the "Looker". "The essential nature of the seen is for his sake" (Wood's translation).

Vivekananda gives this aphorism as "The nature of the experienced is for him", but both writers come to the same conclusion, namely that the whole purpose of nature is for the sake of the Purusha.

Aphorism II/22 introduces the fact that personal karma also has an effect on others. In other words, the summation of personal karmas for a particular family, group or nation, is the karma of that family, group or nation.

The aphorism states: "Although destroyed for him who has attained his goal (achieved the purpose of his creation) it is not destroyed in itself being common to others (II/22)."

"It is conjunction which causes the realisation of the powers, of what is experienced, and of the Lord of what is experienced (II/23)." When the power of the spirit is joined to the powers of nature, then they become manifest in the physical world. For example, if one completely realised one's spiritual Self, and referred the consciousness to that only, then, the mind being diverted from the body and concentrated elsewhere, one would not be conscious of bodily reactions, e.g. heat, cold, pain, pleasure.

Aphorism II/24 states that "Ignorance is the cause". It is due to ignorance the man confuses his physical self with his Real Self, whereby mind is chained to body and suffers accordingly.

"Where ignorance is absent there is no conjunction and the Looker has gained independence (detachment) (II/25)."

Aphorism II/26 tells us that "The means of destruction of ignorance is through continual and continuous discrimination."

"His knowledge is then sevenfold (II/27)." There are seven stages of wisdom, each one unfolding as knowledge grows. The first stage is the feeling of thirsting after knowledge, the final stage arrives when the mind ceases to be dissatisfied and ceases from further seeking.

We come now to some of the most important aphorisms in Patanjali Sutras, namely II/28–32 for these contain the principal "do's" and "don'ts" which form the basic rules for behaviour, through which one may expect to attain Self-Realisation.

II/28 states: "Through performance of Yoga impurities are

destroyed and knowledge grows to the fullness of Discrimination."

II/29 names the Eight Limbs of Yoga which have become famous as the basic requirements for the would-be Yogi, and which must be followed and adhered to throughout. Bodily and mental strength and purity follow as an essential structure on which the powers of the Yogi can be built. Without strength of body, mind and character, the student is in danger of physical and moral damage, which can be of terminal severity.

The Aphorism states: The Eight Limbs of Yoga are:

1 Yama – do's – (see aphorism 30)
2 Niyama – don't's – (see aphorism 32)
3 Asana – postures – as in Hatha Yoga
4 Pranayama – breath control – as in Hatha Yoga
5 Pratyahara – sense control – withdrawal of senses – as in Raja Yoga
6 Dharana – concentration ⎫
7 Dhyana – meditation ⎬ Samyama – as in Raja Yoga
8 Samadhi – contemplation ⎭

Aphorism II/30 gives Yama as abstinence; from Injury to others, lying, theft, continence, greed. These are referred to as "the five Abstinences of Yama".

Aphorism II/31 makes it clear that "These Abstinences are great vows which may not be broken for time, place, purpose or rules of caste (personal circumstance)".

In Aphorism II/32 we are given the positive actions as the Five Observances. "Purification, internal and external, contentment, body control and sensual control, study and attentiveness to God."

Mental control is taught in Aphorism II/33 as "When thoughts arise which are antagonistic to Yoga, contrary thoughts should be introduced." (Here, again we see a reference to Patanjali's basic tenet that "Yoga is control of ideas in the mind" (I/2).)

In II/34 we are given "Obstructions to Yoga", as killing, lying and similar actions, whether they are carried out, caused or approved of, through greed, anger or ignorance, in however great or small a degree. They result in pain, misery and error. This constitutes a "thought to the contrary".

Aphorism II/35 states: "Where non-injury is achieved all enmities cease."

II/36   "Where truth is established the fruits of endeavour are obtained (for himself and others) without the works."

II/37   "When non-theft is achieved the reward is wealth."

II/38   "When continence is achived health and vigour are gained."

II/39   "When nongreed is achieved past-lives are perceived."

II/40   "Bodily health and detachment arise from body cleanliness."

II/41   "Self-Realisation and sense mastery arise from mental cleanliness."

II/42   "The greatest happiness comes from contentment."

II/43   "Powers of the body and sense arise from mortification."

II/44   "Realisation of the Deity comes with repetition of Mantra."

II/45   "Contemplation arises from attentiveness to God."

Further instructions are now given with respect to Asanas:

II/46   "Posture must be firm and pleasant."

II/47   "By controlling restlessness and meditating upon the Infinite, this is achieved."

II/48   "Posture being mastered there is no interference from the dualities."

Breath control is now commented upon:

II/49   "After mastery of posture follows breath control."

II/50   "Breath, either inhaling or exhaling is regulated by place, time and number, becoming long or short."

II/51   "A fourth condition arises in which breath (or Prana) is restrained by meditating upon one object."

II/52   "In consequence the covering of the light (of the Chitta) is dissolved."

II/53   "The mind is then fit for Dharana (Concentration)."

II/54   "Pratyahara occurs when mind is detached from senses and its organs take the form of Chitta."

II/55   "Complete control of body organs (control of the senses) then arises."

Section III — Powers of Mind

In the first two sections, Patanjali has dealt mainly with the physical aspects and the basic concepts of concentration and contemplation. The all-important "Eight Limbs of Yoga" are given in Section II, but only the first five, dealing specifically with Abstinences, Observances, and the physical controls of breath and the senses, are elaborated upon in that Section.

Section III, however, deals specifically with the mental powers which lead to psychic phenomena.

We have seen that the combined practice of Concentration, meditation and contemplation are referred to as "Samyama", in which the final state is Samadhi, when the mind is in perfect union with the object of meditation, and true Yoga is achieved.

Aphorism III/1 states: "Concentration (Dharana) is holding the mind steady on one thing or object."

III/2: "Meditation (Dhyana) occurs when there is an unbroken flow of knowledge."

III/3: "Contemplation (Samadhi) exists when the object of meditation alone exists, and all awareness of self disappears."

III/4: "These three together constitute the practice of Samyama when applied to one object."

III/5: "By mastery of Samyama all knowledge comes to Light."

III/6: "Such mastery is only obtained in stages." Here Patanjali warns that we must not expect too much too soon.

In the beginning, the practice of Concentration alone is difficult and is enough to begin with.* Only when Concentration is mastered, is the mind ready to proceed to meditation, and here again, some will find the greatest difficulty.

When one first begins the practice of meditation, the imagination takes hold, and throws up all sorts of pictures and ideas into the mind. The more we try to stop them the stronger they seem to be, and here is the secret.

When the meditation first begins, allow the mind to wander freely as it will, regardless of what thought and images arise (and these can be somewhat surprising!). This gets rid of all the "loose thought" and superficial mental garbage; then we simply rest quietly, watching the play of such thoughts in a detached manner, as one watches a play on a screen.

* For detailed instruction see *Yoga the Key to Life*.

The object of meditation must then be brought before the mind and held as long as possible, but even a few seconds can be quite an achievement for a beginner.

Yogi Sivananda has written that a thought becomes fixed in the mind if held for $\frac{12}{25}$ second, but to achieve a state of deep meditation, the thought (or object) must be held for $1\frac{1}{2}$ minutes.

Aphorism III/7 points out that "These three are more inward than the preceding."

Dharana, Dhyana and Samadhi are concerned with the inner nature, the mental and spiritual, whereas the preceding Limbs, namely Yama, Niyama, Asana, Pratyahara and Pranayama are concerned with the external, physical aspects.

III/8, however, states that "Even these three (Dharana, Dhyana and Samadhi) are external to the seedless." In other words there is an inner, fundamental aspect of man which is even beyond that Samadhi called the "Highest", for even Samadhi itself is of varying degrees, from that in which the universe exists to that in which the Highest may be perceived.

III/9 appears rather involved when it says that "The control-mood is the association of the mind with the control-movement, when there is the decline of the habit-mould of mind-spreading and the use of that control" (Wood). In other words, if we suppress these impulses which disturb the mind or the thought process, and allow only the impulses of control to exist and grow, the modification generated by the control impulse in the movement of control is itself a control, which will lead to the lower order of Samadhi.

III/10: "The flow (of continuous control) becomes steady by habit."

III/11: When the mind becomes concentrated upon one point or object, and interest in many objects declines, a state of contemplation arises."

III/12: The one-pointed condition arises when the mental image which is past and the mental image which is present, are the same."

III/13: "The transformation, properties, characteristics and states of objects and senses are similarly described" (Wood). The mind undergoes a threefold transformation as to form, state and time, and by these changes, similar changes in gross and subtle matter may be understood by comparison and inference. For example a piece of coal when burnt, is transformed into smoke, flame and ash, which are changes of form, each change involving a change in time. The final change is a change of state, namely from solid to gas and heat.

II/14: "That which is acted upon and is transformed, whether in its past, present or future state, is the qualified."

III/15: "Evolution is brought about by the successive transformation."

III/16: Knowledge of the past and the future are gained by practising Samyama on the three kinds of transformation."

III/17: "Words, the meaning of words, and knowledge gained thereby, are ordinarily confused. By practising Samyama or these three, knowledge of all animal sounds is gained."

III/18: "By practising Samyama on previous impressions knowledge of past life is obtained."

III/19: "By practising Samyama on the images (signs) in another's body, there comes knowledge of his mind."

III/20: "The contents of the mind are not known thereby, but the internal state is known."

III/21: Opinion differs as to the translation and the meaning of this Aphorism, For example, Professor Wood translates this as, "Karma is (of two kinds) with and without commencement; by mind poise on these, or from omens, there is knowledge of the latter end (i.e. death)." Wood then relates this aphorism specifically to karma, saying that by concentrating upon personal karma (that which exists and that which is to come), the Yogi can forecast the time of his death.

Vivekananda, however,* put a completely different construction upon this sentence. His translation states:

"By making Samyama on the form of the body, the perceptibility of the form being obstructed and the power of manifestation in the eye being separated, the Yogi's body becomes unseen."

He elucidates this statement by saying that the body does not really vanish, but it will not be perceived by others. The reason he gives is that when the Yogi has attained the power of concentration in which "form and the thing formed have been separated" by doing Samyama on this, "the power to perceive form is obstructed as this perception comes from the junction of form and the thing formed."

This clearly calls for a considerable amount of elucidation,

---

* Raja Yoga – pages 243–4.

but, as we said at the beginning of this chapter, Patanjali's aphorisms are more subject-headings, or a guide to teachers, than instruction in themselves. This particular aphorism leaves so much unsaid that its only use is to inform the student of the extent of the powers of an Adept, and that these are approached through Samyama in an unspecified manner.

Aphorism III/22: Wood continues the theme of his translation of III/21, as, "From concentration upon friendliness etc., arise various kinds of strength." He follows in III/23 with "From concentration upon various kinds of strengths arise the strength of an elephant, etc."

This, surely, is another way of saying that a man becomes what he thinks!

Aphorism III/24 states, "By practising Samyama on the Inner Light comes knowledge of that which is fine (minute and subtle), what is concealed (or obstructed) and what is remote (or far distant)."

III/25: "By making Samyama on the Sun comes knowledge of the world."

III/26: "By making Samayama on the moon comes knowledge of the stars."

III/27: "By making Samyama on the pole-star comes knowledge of their movements."

III/28: "By making Samyama on the navel comes knowledge of the body movements."

III/29: "By making Samyama on the pit of the throat comes cessation from hunger and thirst."

III/30: "By making Samyama on the tortoise tube (that nerve which is called Kurma) comes steadiness of body."

III/31: "By making Samyama on the light which emanates from the top of the head comes sight of Siddhas."

III/32: "By the power of Pratibha comes all knowledge." The meaning of this is that even though a man has not achieved the power of Samyama, all powers can come to him through spontaneous enlightenment, due to his high state of purity. This can be seen also in the lives of some of the Christian Saints.

III/33: "Understanding of minds comes with practising Samyama on the heart."

It will be seen that Aphorisms III/15 to III/33 are intended as a guide to progressive concentration upon certain parts of the body, each of which results in certain psychic powers. The areas concerned are clearly those areas in which lie the Chakras, the psychic centres which control the areas of the body and the functions of that area in which they lie. Mental concentration brings these to life and opens the consciousness to powers of control over their functions.

III/34: "Pleasure is derived from non-discrimination of the soul and that which is Satvic. The two are different as Satvic action is for another. Practice of Samyama upon the Self gives knowledge of Purusha."

All Satvic action is for the benefit of the soul, and when freed from egoism and illuminated spiritually the Satvic Samyama gives self-knowledge.

III/35: "From this arises the state of Pratibha, the psychic senses are opened to sounds, sights, scents and tastes of the higher world."

III/36: "These powers are obstacles to Samadhi."

Here Patanjali gives warning that the Psychic Powers, though of value in the physical world, must only be regarded as a stage in advancement. The student must therefore not linger in this garden of pleasures and powers, for they are but a fascinating byway, a by-product of this stage of advancement. To achieve true Yoga (Samadhi) one must disregard the Psychic Powers in order to penetrate further into the Spiritual.

III/37: "When the cause of bondage of the mind-stuff (Chitta) is known and the operation of its activity is known, the mind of the Yogi can enter into the mind of another."

The personal mind is but a part of the Universal mind, being bound to the individual body by the nerve channels through which it operates. By loosening his own mind from his own nadis (nerve channels) and doing Samyama on the body or mind of another, by virtue of the fact that "all is one", the Yogi can transfer his consciousness into the consciousness of another through the universal Chitta.

III/38: "By conquering Udana the Yogi is freed from drowning, and from harmful contact with mud, thorns, etc., and has the power of levitation."

"Udana is the name of the nerve current governing the lungs and upper parts of the body" (Vivekananda). It is also known as the "upward air" (Wood).

III/39: "By control of Samana (equalising air) comes brightness" (the body can be made luminous).

III/40: "By making Samyama upon the relationship between Akasa, ether and the organs of hearing, sounds from higher worlds are heard."

According to Yoga, the basic substance from which all materials of the universe derive, is a subtle element called Akasa. This aphorism clearly refers to the power of Clairaudience, to attain which, it is necessary to meditate upon the basic substance of Akasa, the ether which is its material manifestation, the psychic organ of hearing, and the physical instruments of hearing which are the ear and air.

This meditation involves a deep consideration of the relationship between these four, on the lines that the ear alone can only react the varying air pressures which the mind knows as "sounds". That part of Buddhi which one may regard as the "psychic ear" then accepts the impulse so generated, upon which it discriminates.

The following two Aphorisms deal with astral travel in a similar manner. In astral travel the Yogi achieves a state of contemplation in which his consciousness is transferred to his astral (or etheric) body. His physical body remains as in sleep, whilst, attached by the "silver cord" the astral body, under control of conscious mind, becomes a vehicle which can traverse space at the speed of light, and which the Yogi uses to appear at will at places far distant from his physical body. There are many authenticated cases of such on record. (See, for example, Wood's *Practical Yoga*, page 176.)

III/41: "By practising Samyama upon the relationship between Akasa, ether and the body, the Yogi attaining the lightness of down, travels through the ether.

III/42: "By practising Samyama on the mind, outside of the body, called 'great disembodiedness', the covering of the light (ignorance) disappears."

III/43: "By practising Samyama on the elements in their subtle and physical forms and their relation with their inherent Qualities (Gunas) and functions, mastery of elements is obtained."

III/44: "From such mastery comes minuteness, supreme Qualities of the body and their indestructibility."

The Yogi has now attained the Eight Powers, namely,

   i To reduce himself to a minute particle

    ii To increase his size at will
   iii To become heavy
    iv To become light
     v To travel in the astral
    vi To rule all created things (a mental control)
   vii To conquer all created things (control of the elements)
  viii Clairaudience and Clairvoyance.

III/45: "By this the body is glorified by beauty, strength and firmness."

III/46: "By practising Samyama upon the life-forces of the organs and their Qualities (Gunas) and functions, control is obtained."

III/47: "By this the body achieves power to move as fast as thought, control of the psychic senses, and control of elements."

III/48: "By practising Samyama on the relation between pure Spirit and Nature, omnipotence and all knowledge is obtained."

III/49: "When even the ideas of omnipotence and knowledge have been given up, independence and freedom (from all bondage) is attained."

III/50: "The Yogi must not feel proud or flattered by the appearance of celestical beings for this will only cause recurrence of Obstacles."

III/51: "By practising Samyama on movements of time, their precessor and successor, arises knowledge of Discrimination."

III/52: "This Samyama will bring discrimination according to places, types and indications, even though these appear similar."

III/53: "Intuitional knowledge is that saving knowledge which covers all things and their modifications."

III/54: "When an equal state of purity exists between Spirit and Intellect, Perfection and Independence (isolation from effects of Nature) is achieved."

Section IV – Independence

IV/1: "The psychic powers are inherent at birth and are attained by drugs, by the power of words, and by the practice of Yoga."

It is taken for granted that belief in reincarnation is accepted as a fact, and that in re-birth, one returns to earth with the

Karma which still remains to be worked out, either good or bad. If one has practised the Eight Limbs of Yoga in a previous life, and has therefore made some advancement on the Path, then in this birth he will enjoy the fruits he has already earned. Among them will be the Siddhis or psychic powers.

The effects of psychedelic drugs is now, alas, too well known to be commented upon, but, as related by Theos Bernard (*Heaven Lies Within Us*, published by Rider & Co.) it is still customary to use drugs in the process of Initiation.

By "the power of words", Patanjali refers to the use of Mantra, sacred words which, under certain conditions, have the power to produce psychic effects.*

IV/2: "Metamorphosis into another form of life is by the filling in of Nature."

This is further explained in the next aphorism:

IV/3: "Deeds, right or wrong (good or bad) do not directly cause metamorphosis but act as removers of obstacles to natural action, as when a farmer clears a ditch for irrigation of a field."

Vivekananda likens this to an irrigation canal in which water already exists, but the farmer must open the gates to allow his fields to be irrigated. Thus we see that the forces (psychic powers) are already present, but it needs some activity on our part to open our "psychic field" to those natural forces.

IV/4: "Artificial minds are created by egoism of the Yogi."

In order to work out quickly all accumulated Karma, the Yogi is said to be able to create different bodies (Kaya-vyuka). Such "created minds" bear the personality of the Yogi and react directly upon the Yogi himself.

IV/5: "The one original mind (that of the Yogi) remains controller of all such created minds."

IV/6: "Of all the minds (of men) only that which has attained to Samadhi (perfect contemplation) is free from desires and is the highest."

IV/7: "The works of the Yogi are neither black nor white (neither good nor bad). For others they are threefold, black, white and a mixture of both."

IV/8: "From such threefold works are manifested only those desires suitable to that state."

Reference is intended here to Sanskaras and their Karmas.

IV/9: "Even though separated by space, time and species

* See *Yoga The Key to Life*.

there is still continuity of desires due to Sanskaras and memories."

IV/10: "Thirst for happiness is eternal; desires have no beginning."

All desires are basically a search for happiness. This is inherent, even at birth, and most of our thought and activity is directed to achieving that end. To quote Vivekananda, "each fresh experience is based upon the tendency generated by a past experience, therefore desire is without a beginning."

IV/11: "Because it is held together by cause, effect, support and object, when these are absent, it also is absent."

IV/12: "What is past and what is to come, in their own nature according to their Qualities (Gunas)."

IV/13: "They are subtle or manifest according to their Gunas."

IV/14: "There is unity in all things because of the unity within the change." Here Patanjali is saying in effect that "all is one" for although all things have different characters and nature according to their Qualities, basically, their fundamental substance (Akasa) is the same, each being but a modification of that fundamental substance, but in differing degrees, according to their natural rate of vibration.*

IV/15: "Minds differ in degree of perception with regard to the same object, and mind and object are of a different nature."

IV/16: "Things become known or unknown to the mind depending on whether they are cognised by the mind."

IV/17: "A thing can be known or unknown to the mind depending upon the modification of the mind."

The mind may perceive an object, but does not "know" the object until it has been experienced, which has then "coloured" or modified the mind-stuff.

IV/18: "The mind and its contents are always known to its owner for this (the owner) is the unchangeable Purusha."

The Purusha, in relation to mind, is stationary, for the mind is always in movement because of the ideas which modify its substance. The Purusha is therefore in a position to regard the mental modifications as a spectator watches the movements of a play.

IV/19: "The mind is not luminous of itself as it is itself an object."

* See *Yoga The Key to Life*.

Purusha alone is self-luminous, its power acting through all physical matter and natural forces.

IV/20: "There is no cognition of both (mind and Purusha, or Looker and object) simultaneously."

The mind, not being self-luminous, cannot cognise itself and another object at the same time.

IV/21: "Assuming there exists (in man) a second cognising mind, further cognitions would arise, resulting in confusion."

If we assume one mind watching another, there would have to be a third to cognise the second and a fourth to cognise the third and so ad infinitum. Memory not being held at any one point, confusion would result.

IV/22: "When mind (in contemplation) takes on the form of the higher mind (Purusha) it then becomes conscious of the higher mind."

In contemplation the Purusha is reflected on the conscious mind as in a mirror so that it then sees itself momentarily as the Purusha.

IV/23: "Coloured by the Looker and the object, mind has understanding of all."

Because the reflection of Higher mind (as in IV/22) and because of its cognition of the physical world, the mind is therefore capable of knowledge of both worlds.

IV/24: "The mind, with all its modifications and desires, acts for another because it works in combination (with the Purusha)."

Mind cannot work for itself alone, its function is to serve its owner.

IV/25: "For those with the power to discriminate there is a turning away from mind as Spirit."

The discriminating know that mind is different from Purusha (Spirit).

IV/26: "Having achieved Discrimination the mind achieves Independence (or Isolation)."

IV/27: "Other thoughts arise occasionally from past Sanskaras (habit-moulds)."

IV/28: "Destruction of Sanskaras is the same as for Sources of Trouble as said before."

IV/29: "He who has arrived at Perfect Discrimination and has given up all desires achieves that state called the Cloud of Virtue."

IV/30: "From this all pain ceases and there is freedom from Karmas."

IV/31: "Knowledge then becoming freed from all coverings and impurities becomes infinite and that which is to be known becomes small."

IV/32: "From this comes the end of the transformation due to the Qualities (Gunas) for they have achieved their object."

IV/33: "The changes which occur in moments are perceived at the end of succession (of ideas and moments)."

Thoughts change with each moment, but the result of a succession of such changes can only be seen as a conclusion at the end of a series (or succession) of changes. For the mind which has achieved Omnipresence, time ceases to be, everything exists in the "now", past, present and future are seen as one.

IV/34: "Isolation (or Independence in terms of complete personal freedom) is achieved when the Qualities (Gunas) have completed their purpose. There is full knowledge in its own nature."

The Soul has now experienced all that Nature (through the Qualities) can teach. In the process of learning, the Soul has evolved through higher and higher planes until it is at last fully conscious of itself in its own nature and the Yogi has achieved full Realisation of Self.

Patanjali has now taken us through the full cycle of experience, teaching how, from the very first steps of self-control to the final stages of Samadhi, every individual may attain to full Spiritual Consciousness while still incarnate.

Part 2

Concepts and Applications

CHAPTER 6

Samsara – Reincarnation – Karma – Mukti – Pavritti Marga – Nivritti Marga

We have now considered the principal Sacred Scriptures of ancient India upon which the Philosophy of Yoga is founded and through which it has flowered to the world-wide science of spiritual and physical evolution which we know today.

The Upanishads, the Gita, Patanjali's Sutras, although providing a foundation and a framework are by no means the sole sources of Yoga's philosophy. The works all through the ages of the great Yogis such as Milarepa, Ramakrishna, Aurobindo, Vivekananda, Ramana Maharshi and countless others, have added further knowledge and experience to the literature of Yoga, and further enlightenment on the Path.

Herein lies one of Yoga's great advantages, for, whereas all the great religions are founded on the teaching of one man, now long deceased, and the teachings are therefore open to misinterpretation, wrong translation, and human error over the years, the knowledge taught in Yoga is confirmed and added to in every age by the experience of every Self-Realised individual who has opened the door to the Infinite.

The basic Philosphy has not changed in spite of its years, and all the experiences of the Self-Realised down the ages, from the earliest Rishi to the most recent Yogis, only confirm the traditional teachings. What we have considered in our earlier chapters confirms the basic Philosophy on which Yoga now stands and upon which it has stood unchanged through countless generations.

Having glanced at the main stream of the Philosophy, it may be an advantage to consider now some of the principal beliefs, which are a corollary to the ancient scriptures, and upon which its Yogas are based.

The first of these must be the belief in re-birth, or Reincarnation as it is more generally known. Without a firm belief in re-birth, the whole structure of Yoga collapses, for re-birth and the Law of Karma are the very keystones of the Philosophy to which all Yoga is related.

The thoughts occur to everyone at some time in their life, "Where did I come from? Is there survival after death? What happens when the body dies?"

It is a fact that practically all the Eastern races believe in re-birth indeed, in terms of numbers, more than half the world's population have accepted the premise of re-birth and Karmic Law, but the western world with its scientific approach, has found it hard to accept something which cannot be proved, and Christianity, the religion of the West, denies it.

But now there is hope, for evidence is coming to light from all quarters, of people who have conscious memory of previous lives. There are now so many well authenticated cases of pre-birth memory, which have been published in books and journals in both East and West, that they need not be recounted here.*

Pythagoras is quoted as saying that he remembered, not only past lives, but past names, whilst eminent men of recent times such as Sir Oliver Lodge, Emerson, Walt Whitman, and others also claim such recollection.

The Fathers of the Early Christian Church are said to have accepted the teaching of re-birth, which was only changed by the Second Council of Constantinople in the year A.D. 553.

St. Augustine asks the question, "Did I not dwell in another body . . . before I entered by mother's womb?"

Origen was even more definite when he declared that John the Baptist was Elias re-incarnated, arguing this from the Gospel of Matthew, Chapter XI/14 which says "If ye will receive it, this is Elias which was for to come."

Again, in Chapter XVII/12–13 Matthew reports: "But I say to you Elias is already come and they know him not. . . . Then the disciples understood that Jesus spoke of John the Baptist."

Similar quotations can be found in Mark Chapter VI/14 and Luke Chapter IX.

A belief in re-birth rationalises many of life's apparent

* For example see *Many Mansions* by Dr. G. Geminara (published by Neville Spearman).

anomalies if it is taken with a similar belief in the Laws of Karma. The reason for apparent inequalities of birth and circumstances become clear when it is accepted that our circumstances today are the result of decisions and actions taken previously.

If a child is born into happy affluence, this is taken as the fruit of the good deeds of a previous life. If a child is born into difficult circumstances, it is due to the Karma of past lives which has still to be worked out, or to a lesson which still has to be learned.

Referring to the man born blind, the Disciple asked of Jesus (John IX/2) "Who did sin, this man or his parents, in that he was born blind." To which Jesus replied, "Neither hath this man sinned nor his parents, but that the work of God may be made manifest."

Jesus pointed directly, here, to what was a karmic effect, in other words, that this was an effect of events which had occurred in a previous life, worked out in accordance with the Laws of God.

Also, as a further example in Christian belief in karmic effect, one may take Jesus' retort to the impotent man at the pool of Bethesda, to whom Jesus said, "Behold thou art made whole. Go and sin no more lest a worse thing come to thee (John V/14)."

If we accept that suffering has a purpose and effort is not wasted, life becomes full of hope and meaning. Man is then seen to be the arbiter of his own destiny, with the gift of free will to choose his way of life, to design his own future. The way in which he makes his decisions automatically shapes his future in full accordance with Karmic Law.

Apparent injustices and inequalities then disappear, and the Laws of God are seen to be right and just. Without this, it is impossible to reconcile a just God with inequalities of life, also when it is seen that man is a creature of free will, with an active intelligence, two further points emerge. Firstly, man is not an automaton, but is, as we have said, an arbiter of his own destiny. Secondly, this being so, it is urgent and essential that man makes himself aware of the facts, before he destroys himself in sheer ignorance.

However, it is not our purpose in this book, to either prove or disprove the teaching of re-birth, but to outline the Philosophy of Yoga, a philosophy which can show a way of life by which man can reach to the very Infinite.

In his evolutionary journey, then, we are taught that man passes through this world many times, in order that he may evolve into a finer being, and, in the ultimate, find that Unity with the Creator which is the goal of Yoga and of all religions.

This cycle of birth-death-rebirth, in which the soul passes through this world and the finer worlds, is called Samsara, and the passing of souls Samsriti.

In the Gita (Chapter IV/5) we read, "The Blessed Lord said: Many are my past lives, and thine also Arjuna," and in Chapter II/27, "Of that which is born, death is certain of that which is dead, birth is certain."

The teaching of the Gita is that man returns to earth again and again, until the last lesson is learnt, and man is refined to a state of manifested Divinity. Until perfection is achieved man is in bondage to the cycle of birth and death, and to all the things of the physical world and the physical body. When perfection is achieved, then the Self-Realised man has reached the state of Mukti or Liberation – freedom from the bondage of the flesh and the cycles of Samsara.

In order to visualise more clearly the process of Samsara, this may be set out as shown in Figs. 1, 2 and 3 as follows:

Fig. 1 shows how the individual personality is developed by being acted upon by forces generated by thoughts, actions, environment and circumstance.

Taking these individually we see that

  i Everyone is born with certain inherent traits and dispositions, some inherited and involved in the person's genes, some brought over from previous Karma, some individual "gifts" (which everyone has).
 ii We pick up ideas from the Cosmic mind; thought, forces and ideas of others being transmitted through the universal "chitta" (mind-stuff) to be picked up by individual minds attuned to attract such impulses.
iii Reactions from our own thoughts
 iv Reactions from physical stimuli
  v Reactions from our environment
 vi Reactions to other people

All of these combine to mould character and personality, and

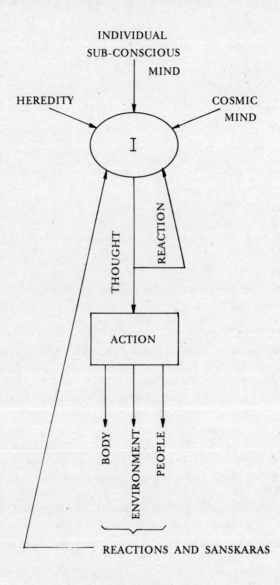

Fig. 1. Sanskaras and Reactions

the mechanism being known by which this operates, control may be established to build ourselves into the kind of person we wish to be and the kind of destiny we wish for ourselves.

Fig. 2 shows the principle of Samsara or Rebirth, and the operation of Karmic influence and Sanskaras upon individual development.

We may take the case of the soul, "I", being incarnated as a boy in Life 1 during which he undergoes experiences and acquires knowledge which will expand his consciousness and personality.

In due course his body wears out and dies, his soul then returning to the world of Spirit for refreshment, re-assessment and further development.

His re-assessment shows that there are still some weaknesses to be overcome, some further knowledge and experience necessary for his approach to perfection, so that he is born again into Life 2, in circumstances designed to give him the knowledge and experience he requires.

This second life may be quite different from the first in terms of race, affluence and even sex, depending entirely upon what experiences he requires for perfection.

This system of birth-death-re-birth (or Samsara as we now know it) continues until a stage is reached when further earth experience is no longer necessary, but experience and knowledge of a higher kind is now required.

The same cycle of Samsara is then pursued on a higher plane.

Fig. 3 shows the complex structure of the "whole man", the interaction of his various planes of activity. It is worthy of deep meditation, whereby the function of each may be assimilated.

This is particularly helpful in attaining to that detachment which is an essential prelude to discrimination and right judgement.

The central teaching of the Shastras is that every man must strive towards Mukti (Liberation), and that all man's striving for happiness, possessions and power are in fact the inner urge which drives man to seek his Real Self, where he will know the true happiness which comes with Liberation. It is only through ignorance that man confuses worldly ambition for the inner urge to find happiness within himself. Now it can be seen why the old Masters taught that ignorance is man's greatest sin – for it divides him from his true self, it alienates him from his Creator.

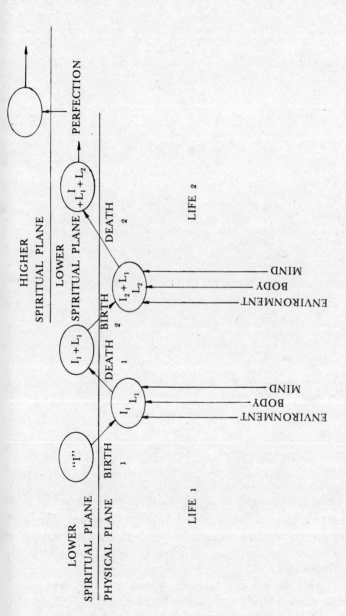

Fig. 2 Reactions and Samsara

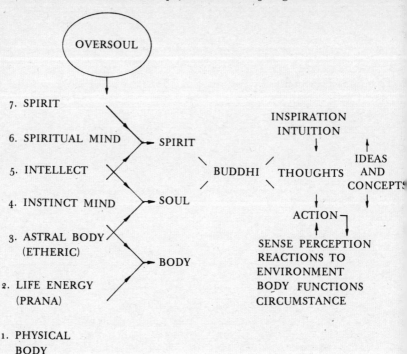

Fig. 3 The seven parts of man related to body, soul and spirit and their interactions

The Philosophy of Yoga is, in fact, a course of training, physical, mental and spiritual, graded from the very earliest beginnings for the most raw neophyte to the deepest philosophical truths in which man's true Self is Realised.

The first step towards Liberation is mental re-orientation, in which the mind is turned away from physical desires, worldly ambitions and attractions, and is turned towards the inner self and the life of the Spirit.

This is known as a "turning about in the seat of Consciousness, and can be represented graphically as in Fig. 4.

To this end discrimination must be exercised on thoughts passing through the mind, with particular emphasis on those

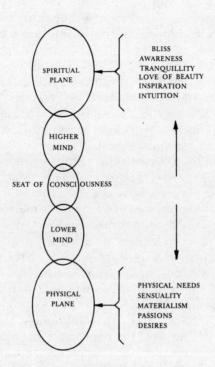

BLISS
AWARENESS
TRANQUILLITY
LOVE OF BEAUTY
INSPIRATION
INTUITION

SPIRITUAL PLANE

HIGHER MIND

SEAT OF CONSCIOUSNESS

LOWER MIND

PHYSICAL PLANE

PHYSICAL NEEDS
SENSUALITY
MATERIALISM
PASSIONS
DESIRES

Fig. 4 Lower mind absorbs impulses from physical sources which generate mental images creating an urge to act upon their suggestion. Desires created in this way may be normal to physical needs but may deteriorate to passions and sensual desires. Higher mind absorbs impulses from the higher spheres creating love, tranquillity, creative ability and spiritual gifts.

Man is free to choose whether he will be dominated by his lower elements or whether he will orientate to the higher plane, by which his mind may become a powerful force, harmonising with, and operating upon, universal natural laws and forces.

leading to desires. Reaction against enjoyment of the senses
cannot come about immediately but can only be the result of a
long and arduous struggle. Like a young and spirited colt which
fights against the controlling bridle, the senses will similarly
revolt against control, and there will be many falls and failings
before the "wild horses" of the senses can be brought under
control.

The purpose of sense control is to establish eventually a state
of purity and strength, in which the Spirit can manifest itself.
Without such state man cannot be receptive of the higher
vibration of Spirit, whilst there is also physical danger from
psychic forces liberated which can maim and destroy where they
are not understood and controlled.

As a preliminary step to the more formal teaching of the
Schools of Yoga, what is known as "Pavritti Marga" or the Path
of Desire, is recommended to the neophyte.

Whilst allowing freedom of choice in the matter of desires, the
mind of the neophyte is turned towards an appreciation of
spiritual values and desires of a higher nature. Elementary
disciplines of mental control are introduced, such as the control
of undesirable habits, and the mechanism by which habits are
formed, by which also they can be controlled once the
mechanism is understood.

The Upanishads teach that, although the riches and
enjoyments of the world can produce happiness, this is as
nothing compared to the happiness of the Spirit. The
Taittiriyaka – Upanishad – (Valli II/8) says.

> Now this is the meaning of Bliss (ananda).
> If there be a young man of noble birth, well versed in the
> Vedas, athletic and strong, with all the world's wealth
> available to him, this is one measure of human bliss.
> One hundred times that bliss is the measure of the saint who is
> free from desires. (Spiritually Realised)

The Upanishad continues to enumerate the degrees of bliss
through the hierarchy of men and Gods, but the message is
clear, that true and lasting happiness can only be found in the
Life of the Spirit, all else is transitory and of no lasting
satisfaction, terminating in any case with death.

The Shastras teach discrimination towards desires, for some
are good and are to be encouraged whilst others are bad and

lead to spiritual death. According to the laws of Karma, good deeds are to be encouraged, for they bring merit and bear good fruit, though we are warned that meritorious deeds must not be performed with the thought of reward.

Acts of self-sacrifice for the help of others, or acts of devotion to God, are enjoined by the Shastras. Such acts are called Yajnas, and in charitable works, in giving to others from our own store of happiness or worldly things, then these are replaced many times over if they are given freely and in the right frame of mind.

The acts of sacrifice (or Yajnas) as given in the Shastras are five-fold:

i	Dava-yajna: prayer and worship of God	} Ritual and Sacrifice
ii	Pitri-yajna: veneration of the Fathers (Ancestors)	
iii	Rishi-yajna: veneration of the Rishis (seers and saints)	
iv	Nri-yajna: service to our fellow men	} Acts of Charity
v	Bhuta-yajna: service to living creatures (birds and beasts, etc.	

It will be seen that, through the yajnas the Shastras teach that prayer, worship, self-sacrifice and charity must be observed by those who tread the Path of Desire (indeed, by all spiritual aspirants). It must not be thought that the disciplines of Pavritti-Marga call for a life of asceticism in which there could be little of happiness. On the contrary, it is taught that the very practice of such discipline brings with it an incomparable happiness, that the world itself can be enjoyed with greater pleasure. Its beauties are seen clearly through the eyes of purity, and God speaks to us through the beauty of all His Creations;

> "Blessed are the pure in heart,
> for they shall see God."

Pavritti-Marga, therefore, offers the means whereby the "turning about in the seat of consciousness" can be achieved, and through a continual examination of desires and practice of the Yajnas, we can become reorientated to the Spirit where true happiness abides and which is the source and the goal of true desire.

This, then, is the Path for the neophyte, for one whose acceptance of the Creator and life-after-death is but recent, and who, therefore, must take the first steps towards purification and spiritual strength.

The Mundaka Upanishad (Second Khanda /912) says "(8) Fools who live in ignorance puffed up with vain knowledge and their own conceit, go round in circles and stagger to and fro as blind men leading the blind.

"(9) Children consider themselves happy having lived long in ignorance. Those who depend on the charity of others are improvident; suffering the penalty of their passions they fall and die in misery.

"(10) Believing that sacrifice and charitable works are enough, the ignorant, having no higher knowledge and having already reaped the rewards of their own good works, enter again to life on this earth.

"(11) But those who practise penance and faith, living in charity and wisdom in tranquillity (free from passion) depart (this life) to where the Immortal Person dwells, whose nature is eternal.

"(12) Let a Brahmana . . . acquire freedom from all desires. That which is eternal cannot be gained by what is temporal. Let him, in order to understand this, approach a Guru who has Knowledge and who is one with Brahman."

The Upanishad makes it clear that, knowledge of the physical world alone is not enough. Even though we fill our minds with all the available knowledge of God and spiritual life, we are but as blind men, and such knowledge is of no true lasting value.

It teaches also that, even though we have some spiritual knowledge and offer sacrifice and do good works, as long as desires exist, the sacrifices and the good works have only the limited value of rewards immediately consequent upon such acts. In other words the satisfaction of performing such deeds constitutes its own reward. If, on the other hand, such deeds had been carried out with no sense of personal satisfaction (or "without thought of the fruit thereof"), then the rewards would accrue in the form of good karma.

The final paragraph of the Khanda is rather misleading and cannot be taken literally when it states that "That which is eternal cannot be gained by what is temporal", for we are told in another place that "By what men fall, by that they rise". In other words, by overcoming a weakness we gain strength and without such weakness the opportunity to exercise will and to grow in strength, would not exist. The lesson of the Khanda is that in order to gain the Eternal, we must use those parts of our make-up which are Eternal, for the Spirit can only be seen with the eyes of the Spirit.

In his passage through the Path of Desire (Pavritti Marga) man realises that it is these very desires which chain him to the endless cycle of Samsara. He realises also that desires can never be satisfied, that they can only breed pain, disillusionment and frustration. Desire breeds further desire and so creates habits which, in the end, control the man.

So it is learnt through painful experience that the pleasures of the senses cannot bring lasting happiness, that even when a desire is fulfilled, the thirst for it still remains. And so man is lead to shun the desires which have hurt him, and in his disillusionment he turns away from the things of the world to the things of the inner life in which he begins to find more peace and satisfaction.

In meditating upon these things, man begins to find a peace and tranquillity he has never before known, and as the Spirit opens out within him he begins to feel that "Peace which passeth all understanding".

In the Katha Upanishad (II/1) we read:

"God created man's senses so that they look forward so man looks outwards and not within himself. Some seer, with eyes closed, meditating upon Immortality saw the Real Self within."

So it is that man leaves the Path of Desire (Pavritti Marga) to tread the Path of Renunciation (which is Nivritti Marga). For those in search of the Spirit, Renunciation of things of this world is the first step.

"Give up all thou hast and follow me," said Jesus.

"Enjoyment of the world and enjoyment of God can never go together," said Vivekananda.

"If you desire to attain God, you must renounce possessions and passions," said Ramakrishna.

So man must find his own way to the Spirit, through trial and tribulation, through sacrifice and sorrow, through pain and peril. But at the end, the reward is great, and though the way is hard and long, yet there is an inner radiance, an all pervading happiness, in knowing and feeling that one is moving towards that state of bliss which is so great that it is beyond man's powers to describe. There is nothing in man's experience with which it

can be compared, and so he has no words with which to name it
or to tell of it.

As all men are different, and all have different needs, no two
people being in exactly the same state, no single path can be laid
down which will suit everyone, so that different paths have been
developed to suit different types of individuals.

These paths are called Yogas so named because the word
means "Unity" or "to join", and their goal is Union with God in
which the individual Spirit is "joined" with its Creator.

Many different Schools of Yoga have developed through the
ages, but each has been designed to suit a particular type of
individual, for although every individual is different in some
respects, there can be general classification of groups.

The Gita teaches four kinds of Yoga, Raja Yoga, Bhakta Yoga,
Jnana Yoga and Karma Yoga, and references to each are
scattered throughout the Gita. For a general description of
other forms of Yoga, the reader is referred to *Yoga the Key to Life*,
but here we must include one more School, that of Hatha Yoga.

We may list the principal Yogas as follows:

Hatha Yoga – the Yoga of physical perfection and the
    arousing of Kundalini
Raja Yoga – for the intellectual
Bhakta Yoga – devotional – prayer, sacrifice, ritual
Jnana Yoga – knowledge (physical and occult)
Karma Yoga – for the man of action

All the Yogas are but separate paths leading to the same goal,
they differ only in their method and the "area" in which they
operate.

Swami Nirvedananda* tabulates the types of Yoga according
to types of men. "Karma", he says, "is for the man of action,
Jnana for the rationalists, Bhakta for the emotional type and
Raja for the empiricist." It is always recommended that the
neophyte seek out a Guru who will advise him which course of
Yoga is best suited to his needs. But a Self-Realised Guru is
extremely difficult to find, and the sadhaka must rely, in the
meantime, upon what is immediately available in the form of
books and lectures. He must, in any case, practise meditation
and inner searching, for it is from the inner source that
guidance, intuition and inspiration spring.

* *Hinduism*, published by Ramakrishna Mission.

Even the Path of Renunciation need not be absolute in the first beginnings, as it is not for everyone to give up possessions and worldly enjoyments to become a recluse, a monk or a nun. All the great religions of the world offer what is, in fact, a graded path to Spiritual Attainment. Whilst Civil Law protects the individual and his property, the Laws of the Churches protect the Spirit and lead to a state of Spiritual Bliss and Union, as one can see repeated so many times in the lives of saints of all denominations and all creeds.

The essential duty for every man is a mental orientation towards the Spirit, for only by living a spiritual life can true happiness be found. Only by following the Karmic Laws of the Creator can be found that "Peace which passeth all understanding."

CHAPTER 7

The Physical Approach – Hatha Yoga

It is remarkable that although the existence of Yoga can be traced back for 4000 years and more, so little has percolated through to the western world until comparatively recently. Even now, if one expresses an interest in Yoga, almost invariably one is asked, "Do you stand on your head?" Or perhaps the more widely travelled will say, "Oh yes, I've seen these Yogis sitting almost naked, filthy dirty, sticking needles in themselves or with one arm in the air for such a long time that it had withered. I think Yogis are misguided cranks."

The first statement can be regarded as a cynicism born of ignorance, whilst the second is an opinion formed by a superficial, fleeting impression. It is true that there is much in true Yoga which can be off-putting at first glance, but even from what has been said in our previous chapters, it must be clear that Yoga is a most penetrating and serious business, calling for a strong desire to KNOW, backed up by perseverance and diligence. Only by such application can the rewards of physical, mental and spiritual health and harmony be achieved.

The half-naked gentleman with the elevated arm referred to, was, in fact, not a Yogi at all. He was a "Fakir", a word which means a "Penitent", and many examples of such may be seen in all parts of India. The publicly exposed Fakir is a direct contradiction to the true Yogi, who is extremely difficult to find, shuns publicity, and rarely allows himself to be seen unless there is a particular reason. Also, he is the epitome of purity and cleanliness, both physical and mental.

A Fakir is one who has at some time been attracted to the study and practice of Yoga, and has become absorbed with the practice of self-inflicted suffering as a means of neutralising old, "bad" Karma, and who is practising extremes of self-control as a means of gaining mental ascendancy over the physical body. In so doing, the Fakir has become diverted from the teaching of true Yoga, which insists upon moderation in all things. The Gita tells us we should have, "not too much sleep nor too little, not too much food nor too little", and generally indicates the "Middle Way" taught by the Buddha.

There is little spiritual benefit in self-inflicted torture, a fact which has been proved in the Christian Church, for severe physical hardship holds the mind in the physical sphere, whence, being so trapped, it cannot perform that "turning about in the seat of Consciousness", which directs perception to the Spiritual. This does not mean, of course, that we may become self-indulgent but, even as an athlete will become soft without exercise, so in Yoga self-discipline is necessary to develop will-power, a strong mind, a healthy body.

The basic form of Yoga with which one normally begins, is HATHA YOGA, which is the approach to the spiritual through the physical. Being principally directed to the body, Hatha Yoga commences with objectives which can be readily observed, and upon which improvements can immediately be perceived and felt. The body-mind relationship (psychosomatic responses) is now known to be a system of congruent, interacting forces, which can be co-operative or otherwise, their mutual effects being well known to the medical profession. In Hatha Yoga these interacting forces are used to develop a healthy relationship between mind and body, in which tensions disappear, blood pressure and nervousness are controlled, mobility and muscular development are carried to perfection. Vitality and youthfulness, mental harmony and poise are the rewards for effort, a perfect balance of mind and body becomes reflected in peace, tranquillity and efficiency.

In his book, *Hatha Yoga*, Professor Shyam Sundar Goswami gives personal verification of the effects of regularly practising Hatha Yoga. One Kali Singh, for example, a practising Hatha Yogi, lived to be over 110 years, and remained in excellent health almost to his last days, whilst K. Rammurti (who specialised in Pranayama – breathing practices), was able to support an elephant upon his chest. Professor Goswami himself relates how, from an ailing child, he was able to so develop his own physique by practising Hatha Yoga, that even iron tongs could make no impression upon his contracted muscles. Also, by contracting his throat muscles, he could withstand the combined efforts of twelve men pulling upon a chain around his throat.

These are, of course, the more spectacular effects of Hatha Yoga, but these are not the real goal of true Yoga. The aim is not just physical perfection. A weak or ailing body is not a proper instrument for the developed mind, and if the body is strong, vigorous and healthy, then a state of mental harmony can more easily be achieved, and one is more able to concentrate upon the difficulties which exist in trying to achieve control on the mental plane. If the mind is constantly harassed by bodily irritations and discomforts, it can never achieve that tranquillity which is essential to the practice of meditation and the more advanced studies of Yoga.

Some Yogic practices, particularly in Tantric Yoga, are directed to arousing occult forces, and this can be very dangerous to the uninitiated. For example, some exercises are directed specifically to developing the psychic centres of the body (the Chakras), their purpose being to raise the Kundalini Power. This, sometimes called the "Sleeping Serpent", is situated at the base of the spine, the purpose of the exercises being to awaken this Power and to direct it through the psychic channels along the spine to the "Thousand Petalled Lotus" in the head.

Such practices must only be carried out under expert guidance and after considerable previous preparation. Several years of intensive study and discipline are necessary, and such are outside the scope of this book and are not recommended to the casual student.

Yoga is essentially practical in its physical approach, and although it aims at the highest achievement possible to man, it begins its teaching with the practical aspects of morals and behaviour. The first step is a reorientation of one's mental outlook, which must be based upon the fact that Man is essentially and primarily a spiritual being, that he has within him the germ of Godhead, and that he must therefore develop a consciousness of being "in the world but not of it".

Remembering also that thought always precedes action, it is evident that the mind must also be prepared by instruction, leading to an understanding of the relationship and interaction of mind and body, so that when an action is undertaken, mental forces can be brought, consciously, to assist the physical forces. This is particularly important in the practice of asanas.

The purifying processes of Yama and Niyama, Asana and Pranayama, will then be able to operate freely and without obstruction, when their beneficial effects upon mind and body will become self-evident. To the practical and penetrating mind of the western student, however, the guide-lines of Yama and Niyama, and the practices of Asana and Pranayama are not sufficient in themselves without explanation and proof, for this is the way in which the western mind has been trained.

The Indian student has previously not been accustomed to question the "why" and the "how" of things, his Guru gave the teaching as facts, established over the years by experience and observation and therefore incontrovertible. Further proof was therefore deemed to be unnecessary. Also there is the probability that the student, whether western or eastern, may not have developed sufficiently to understand the deeper meanings even if they were given, and it therefore becomes the student to accept his Guru's teaching until such time as his own development allows him to come to his own conclusions and prove matters for himself.

The study of Hatha Yoga involves also the study of Human Biology and Psychology, added to those principles which lie behind the code of behaviour, moral life and physical training, which is the backbone of the science of Yoga. This is naturally, a wide field of enquiry, for as we have said previously, the study of Yoga is the study of the *whole* man, but we shall endeavour to cover the main principles which are our principal concern.

In my previous book,* it was shown how the process of evolution has revealed that behind all life there lies a dynamic force which acts upon all living things. It is a creative urge which results in the modification of progeny, and so, over a period of time, produces new forms of ever greater complexity, mobility, efficiency and diversity, enabling each to overcome to a greater extent its own environment and to evolve into a higher form of life. This we called the "Creative Will". It is the urge, the driving force behind evolution.

It is self-evident that evolution has brought us to the advanced state which we now enjoy, by a process of which we have been but dimly aware. The powerful forces which have

* *Yoga The Key to Life*, published by Rider & Co.

been operating on a universal scale to bring life to its present state of development, have been a vital, living background, permeating all life, working upon it and driving it forward to the unfoldment of greater awareness, to a higher state of consciousness. It has been going on for countless thousands of years, yet awareness in the western world of this great manifestation of the Supreme Will has only been awakened generally in comparatively recent years.

The Philosophy of Yoga, however, shows that awareness of this subtle, creative background has been alive in India since the days of the Vedas, in which analysis of man's complex nature and organism was carried out in such detail and accuracy by the ancient Rishis, that modern biology can teach it very little. In analysing man and the subtle "ground" through which he is activated, the ancients found that *every* man has an individual share of this Creative Will, and by applying it to himself, making use of the natural laws which exist upon both physical and subtle planes, man is able to develop and maintain himself well beyond the normal span. This is a fact which can be proved by anyone who is prepared to devote a little time and energy each day to this end.

Let us now look at the effect of the Creative Will upon the human body, and how it has developed this body to its present state.

The basic building bricks of all living things are the cells of which they are formed. The cell, the tiniest living organism, is no more than a speck of protoplasm with a central nucleus. Yet it has an intelligence which enables it to reproduce itself and to develop in various ways, according to the needs directed by its environment and its basic urge to survive. In the course of this process, the cell became modified and diversified, enabling it to perform different functions. The greatest diversification of all lies in the human body. Bone, muscle, nerves, fat, blood and cilliates, are formed of their own special type of cell peculiar to themselves, each different type fulfilling its own particular and specialised function.

This being so, it is evident that these minute building bricks suffer wear in operating the various systems of the body, and it is these which are nourished by the intake of food and air, undergoing a re-charging process when the body is at rest. A further point of importance is that each special group of cells forms a separate organ or part of the body which has its own individual life, but when the life force leaves the body at death then the whole system of cells ceases to function and the body dies.

This activity is a reflection of the events which occur in both microcosm and macrocosm, for as the individual cell is to the organ, so is that organ to the body as a whole. Also, if an organ falls sick, it can often be cured or removed by surgery without affecting any of the remaining organs, except, of course, in the case of a corrosive or malignant disease. Carrying the analogy a step further, one can see each human being as an individual cell, forming one of a particular clan or family. The clan or family then, in turn, form the cells which go to make up a nation, whilst the nations in their turn form the human race. It becomes clear, therefore, that if the individual is defective, his defects tend to spread to other individuals, and in this way a whole race can become contaminated, physically, or psychically in terms of thought patterns which become habits. The effects of such a train of events could be seen only too clearly in the last war, when thought patterns of the individual and the nation were cultivated and directed by carefully planned propaganda.

The importance of the individual to the national organism is self-evident, and underlines the responsibility which every individual has, towards both himself and to the nation into which he was born. It points also to the necessity for administrators and governments to consider man as an individual unit and not as a collective mass, as a living cell whose correct and loyal functioning is vital to the health and prosperity of the larger organism of the nation, and whose individual needs must therefore be given the fullest consideration possible.

However, in Hatha Yoga, the "physical approach to the spirit", we are particularly concerned with the cells which have formed those muscles by which the body moves, and the glands which pass their living streams of nourishment and energy into the system. The life principle itself can be considered as having two forms of expressions: one, the dynamic which expresses itself in movement, and the other, static, expressing itself as a form of consciousness. The life force behind both is "Prana", which is involved in all forms of energy as manifested on the physical plane, and mental activity (in its dynamic form), upon the subtle plane. We have also seen a little of the interaction of these forces; how a mental condition is reflected in a physical condition, and vice versa. It becomes evident, then that in order to obtain a healthy body and a happy state of mind, both forces must operate in harmony in both their static and dynamic states.

Now the muscle cells with which Hatha Yoga is principally concerned, fall into two groups, each of which has its own special function. One group is associated with bodily movements which include locomotion, support, and specific complex movements such as playing a musical instrument, driving a car, painting a picture, running or climbing. The second group is directly concerned with the organic functions of the body, and includes the activities of circulation, assimilation, digestion, excretion and reproduction, the heart being an individual modification of the second group, but included therein. The first group are the "striated muscles", the most obvious of which are the biceps, the second being the so-called "smooth muscles", whilst the cardiac muscle of the heart is made up of a complex network of fine strands, joined together to form its four compartments.

The striated muscles were developed in parallel with the skeletal structure, this first appearing in the fishes of the Devonian Period (some 300 million years ago). These spinal muscles probably were the first form of muscular development, a form which gave fish the ability to swim. The equivalent muscles of the human body are the major motional muscles and have a direct influence upon the nervous system, vital organs, poise and personality. If the skeletal structure or its supporting muscles are deformed or inadequate, then both the physical and psychic aspects of the individual are adversely affected. It is therefore of primary importance to develop and maintain the spinal muscles in peak condition as long as is possible. Reference to Fig. 5 will show these muscles and their importance to the human frame.

In the Carboniferous Period (about 250 million years ago), development had reached the amphibian stage, calling for additional muscles to power the crawling action. Fins developed into limbs, but these were too weak to support the body in their early stages of development; the limbs were stunted, limiting the animal to a crawling motion. Crawling also involved some activity of the spinal muscles, which can be seen by observing the movements of a crocodile.

The Permian Period and the Mesozoic (the Age of Reptiles), a period of development occupying some 150 million years, saw muscular development confined almost entirely to the transfer of locomotion from crawling to near vertical walking, so that forward movement then became an operation of the lower limbs, leaving spinal musculature to develop its own more complex activities. The body was now lifted off the ground, the consequent raising of the head giving a new perspective which developed greater awareness and a growing consciousness.

Several muscle groups were now involved in maintaining the frame in an upright posture, its effectiveness depending then upon muscle tone. The principal muscles involved can be seen in Fig. 5, while Fig. 7a shows the "Cobra" asana, specifically designed to develop this group of muscles.

Consequent upon the upright position, the need now arose to contain and protect vital organs, keeping them in their proper places, so that they could function efficiently. The abdominal wall, the thoracic and subsidiary muscles were then developed, enabling respiration, digestion and trunk movements to be made in the upright position. These muscles can be seen in Fig. 6, for which the "Bow" asana in Fig. 7b has special application.

It was not until about one million years ago, however, in the Pleistocene Period, that those muscles fully developed which allowed man to walk upright and to run. Later Palaeolithic man developed muscles which gave him the ability to carry out the more complex movements of throwing, dancing and a more upright stance. His mental capacity increased withal, mental condition being closely related to physical symmetry as we have seen. The latter point is emphasised in Yoga, special exercises having been developed to provide a supple and well poised frame.

In this brief summary of man's muscular development one can observe a slow but imperative drive towards greater activity and a wider degree of awareness. You may ask at this stage, what is the point of discussing a process of evolution of which everyone is already well aware. The point is that the development of musculature to its present stage has taken some three hundred million years to accomplish, and that when one is aware of the process of the mechanics of growth and development and of the operation of the mind, then the power

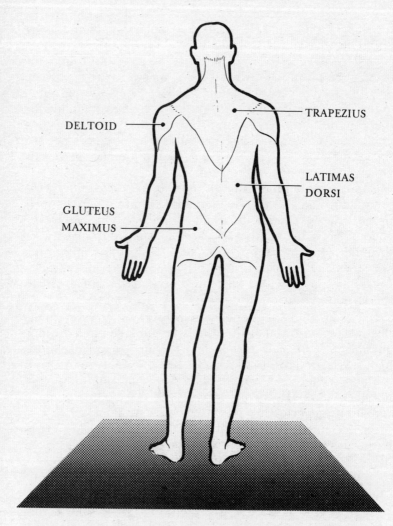

Fig. 5 The principal back muscles

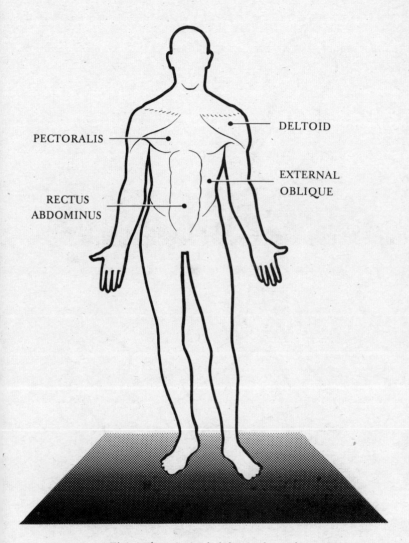

Fig. 6 The principal abdominal muscles

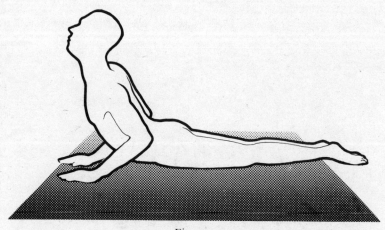

Fig. 7a

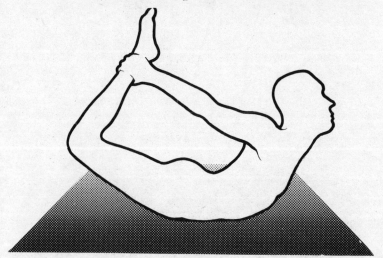

Fig. 7b

of mind can be brought into focus, considerably accelerating development.

In this connection it is profitable to consider for a moment the evolution of a human being from the moment of conception. At the instant of fertilisation, spiritual force has entered into a relationship with physical matter, which it then proceeds to organise into the living organism which we know as a cell (or cells).

The different cells then divide and evolve into groups which form the various organs and parts of the body, finally integrating into the most complex organisation of living matter in the universe – MAN.

The fact upon which we must concentrate our attention is that, although the foetus in the womb has never experienced sight, sound, smell or taste, yet it is able to develop organs which are attuned to receive these vibrations, together with a mind which is able to interpret them.

If one traces Man's evolution back to its very beginnings, there must be found a point at which the potential Man was introduced into the basic protoplasmic cell.

We can therefore perceive, not merely a driving force, a simple directed energy, but an Intelligence which is able to create forms and living organisms, actually IN ADVANCE OF THE NEED FOR THEIR APPLICATION.

It is this Intelligence and the Creative Force which we contact and direct when we practise the asanas of Hatha Yoga in conjunction with controlled mental effort.

This must be fully appreciated, and a clear picture of its operation held in mind.

A study of Raja Yoga in conjunction with Hatha Yoga is to some extent essential, for Raja gives us the techniques of mental control and development, and teaches those processes in which the mind establishes control over the physical processes. We shall discuss these in the next chapter.

So far, we have been concerned only with those parts of the body which give it support and movement. We must now take a look at the more subtle parts by which it is nourished and energised. The work of the lungs in oxygenating and purifying the body, as well as the all-important taking in of Prana with the air we breathe, has already been mentioned, though somewhat briefly. This is, however, one of the major aspects of both physical and mental well-being, and is fundamental to any attempt at self-development in either sphere. This is dealt with fully in my previous book, *Yoga The Key to Life*, and so, in order to reserve space herein for other matters, the reader is referred thereto.

We have seen that it is the cell, the basic building block of the body, which has to be nourished, repaired and replaced. Oxygen is, of course, supplied to the cells by the respiratory system, whilst the proteins, sugar, fats and salts necessary for their maintenance, are supplied by the digestive system.

The 30-foot-long alimentary canal, passing through the torso from mouth to anus and including the stomach and intestines, is now familiar to most, as are the glands which, situated at different positions along the tube, pass their secretions into the food in the digestive process. This is in fact a process of chemical change, in which proteins, carbohydrates, salts and fats, are changed into soluble elements which can be assimilated by the body. Fig. 8a shows an asana called "The Twist", which is designed to give massage and stimulate blood circulation to the internal organs and the spine.

Salts and sugar, being soluble in water by nature, are passed

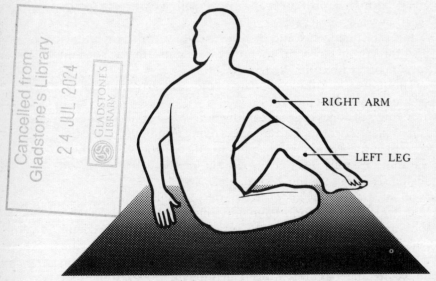

RIGHT ARM

LEFT LEG

Fig. 8a

through the mucous membrane which lines the digestive tract, so passing directly into the bloodsteam which, in turn, feeds the body cells. Proteins, fats and starchy elements of carbohydrates, however, must be converted to soluble elements before they can be absorbed by the body.

The first part of the latter process takes place in the mouth, where food is masticated and mixed with saliva, which converts starchy substances to sugar. Next, the food is acted upon by the gastric juices provided by the peptic glands in the mucous membrane of the stomach, so turning proteins into peptones, which are soluble in water. In the small intestine, the insolubles are acted upon by the pancreas (principally fats), and any work left undone by the saliva and the peptic glands on starches and proteins is completed.

The solution which has now been prepared by the digestive glands is sufficiently fine to pass through the membrane of the digestive tract, into the bloodstream which runs on the other side of the membrane. The bloodstream is contained at this point by fine capillaries which pass the nourishment into the circulatory system, and so to the cells all over the body. This passing of the nourishing food solution into the bloodstream is called "assimilation".

Some absorption also takes place in the colon, and this is why regular and complete elimination is essential to good health, as otherwise, the solution passing into the bloodstream becomes fouled, resulting in a sluggish brain and mind, whilst reducing body tone to a depressing level.

Clearly, if the gastric juices are weak, or the muscular movements of peristalsis are inadequate, dyspepsia will be the result, whilst the ills and dangers of constipation are too well known now to need repetition. To prevent these difficulties or to cure them where necessary, Yoga has provided the asana, "The Plough" (shown in Fig. 10, also known as "Halasana"), The "Twist", shown in Fig. 8a and similar exercises. The importance of the work done by the liver cannot be underestimated, and this, the largest gland of the body, is also maintained in healthy condition by the exercises just given.

From the preceding it will be evident to the reader that, "we become what we eat", and Yoga therefore prescribes certain foods which are health-giving and nourishing, and points out also those which, although tasty and exciting to the tongue, result in irritation of certain parts of the body, an irritation which becomes reflected in temperament and temper. (Details of diet can also be found in my previous book.)

The Bhagavad Gita (18. 29–32), has divided human beings into three groups, according to their characteristics and stage of development. This grouping is based upon the basic qualities (the Gunas) of matter (Prakriti), these three qualities being named Tamas, Rajas, and Satva, all elements of matter containing all three of these qualities, but in varying degree according to their characteristics. Tamas represents that which is dull, heavy, clod-like, lazy and indolent. Rajas represents that which is fiery, passionate, and given to activity, whilst Satva is that which is harmonious, orderly, bland and peaceful.

As all matter possesses some of these qualities in varying degree, it becomes no more than common sense to select our food from those substances which nourish and soothe, rather than those which may be pleasing to the palate, but which are spicy and therefore irritant, or heavy and de-energising. Patanjali in his Yoga Aphorisms says (2–1), "Yoga is active life, consisting of Body-conditioning, Self-study, and Attention to God." Clearly the instruction is to study man in all his parts, and with particular reference to body-conditioning, to know precisely how the body is constructed, the functioning of each of its parts, their proper control and maintenance, and how to develop them to peak efficiency. This is the task fulfilled by Hatha Yoga.

Having digressed for a moment, we must return to our study of the organisation of the body, so that we may know how it may be directed towards perfection. We have seen how musculature has been developed by the action of the Creative Will against environment, and have briefly examined how the cells of the body obtain their nourishment. These are the more obvious aspects of health dealt with by Hatha Yoga, but we must now move on to the more subtle elements which, nevertheless, have a most powerful effect upon mental and bodily health, and even upon bodily structure. This is the Nervous System.

In order that the muscles may perform their proper activities, the organs of the body function correctly, and the whole system be properly coordinated, there must be a controlling principle operating from a central point, sending the necessary signals to motivate the required function. This central point is, of course, the brain, which passes impulses through the nervous system to the part concerned. By this means the muscles are activated to apply the necessary force which moves the limbs, lifts weights, or performs similar mechanical functions. Similar control is necessary to take food into the mouth and to pass it through the complex digestive system in assimilation and excretion, whilst the respiratory and circulation systems take oxygen into the lungs and pass it into the bloodstream, so carrying out the purifying and energising process without which the body would die in a very short time.

There are a total of 43 pairs of nerves in the cranial and spinal systems, and these are distributed throughout the body in a fine network of thread-like fibres, some of which find their nerve-endings at the surface of the skin, giving it that sensitivity which is one of the minor sense-perceptions.

The nervous system has three separate functions, which operate at such a speed that they appear to be simultaneous. They can be listed as follows:

1 The reception of internal and external sensations
2 The intelligent analysis of the sensations
3 Making a decision and acting upon the information received.

Consider for a moment, the sequence of events which must occur when a pianist plays on sight a piece of music he has never seen before. In the first place, his mind has received considerable training to enable it to decipher the system of code-writing which is written music. Through the difference in tones of black and white, and their position relative to two sets of five horizontal lines, impulses are carried to the brain having a certain value of vibration frequency and amplitude. These impulses are examined by the mind, which identifies them as being notes of a certain value and position in the musical scale. The mind then directs the fingers of the two hands, simul-taneously, to press down upon several of the keys on the piano, instructs them as to exactly the pressure they are to exert, at the same time sending via the brain and the nervous system a message to the feet to carry out certain operations on the "loud", or the "soft", pedal, as the music requires. The result is a musical chord, and this action being repeated for every note of music printed on the treble and bass clef lines, produces a continuous stream of sound which we call "music". Watch for a moment, the motions of a concert pianist; think of all the operations involved in producing the music; think of the incredible speed at which the mind must work to produce such coordination, and one experiences awe and humility at the perfection of such a creation.

The nervous system consists of two main groups of nerves, the Central and Peripheral. The first consists of the brain and the spinal chord. The Peripheral Nervous System consists of the 12 pairs of cranial nerves attached to the brain, and the 31 pairs of spinal nerves attached to the spinal cord. The Afferent nerves are those which carry messages of a sensory nature to the brain and to the spinal cord. These are the messages which come from the sensory perceptions, and function on either internal or external stimuli. The Efferent Nerves are the motor nerves which carry messages from the brain and the spinal cord to the organs, glands and muscles of the body, bringing them into operation as desired.

There is a third system of nerves in the body, called the "Autonomous Nervous System", and this again is formed of two distinct groups. The Autonomous System controls the heart, blood-vessels, lungs, digestive system, the genitals and sphincter muscles; in other words, all those parts which operate independently and without conscious thought. The two groups forming the Autonomous System are the Sympathetic and Parasympathetic Systems. The first is composed of two chains of fibres which carry ganglia, and are situated on each side of the vertebral column from the neck to the sacrum. The second is smaller than the sympathetic system, and is itself in two parts, the cranial and the sacral, and makes use of the cranial and sacral nerves for its distribution.

The actions of the two autonomous systems are antagonistic, for whereas one tends to relax, the other stimulates.

The duty of the sympathetic system is to mobilise the resources of the body to meet trouble; the heart is made to beat faster to pass greater quantities of blood, the blood pressure is raised and greater energy is thereby made available, but the digestive system is slowed down. The parasympathetic system is directed more towards the conservation of energy and quieting down the system, though promoting the digestive functions. Under normal conditions, both systems must be maintained in balance.

All the 43 pairs of nerves of the cranial and spinal systems are distributed throughout the body, forming a fine network of thread-like fibres, some of which find their nerve-endings at the surface of the skin, and so giving it that sensitivity which is one of our minor sense-perceptions. The brain acts as a receiving station for the messages passed by the nervous system, and these are passed in turn to "Manas", that part of the mind which analyses, reasons, and applies intelligence.

Our conscious Self, however, the "I", is the final arbiter of all our activities, whether of thought or of action as a result of sense-perception, so that we are therefore confronted with two possibilities. First, we may leave our reactions entirely to the automatic functions of the subconscious, or instinctive system, without applying either reason or will, and so without any form of intelligent control. In this case we will be at the mercy of every whim, sensory urge and fancy which possesses us at any time. We would inevitably become unthinking automatons whose reactions to stimuli would always be mechanical, predictable and automatic, just as the dogs in Pavlov's experiments.

It is a fact that we are so conditioned by our early training at school, in the home, and by everyday living, that by far the greater portion of our thinking and responses to external events and stimuli are automatic. In general, people are so occupied in satisfying their desires and amibitons, seeking ever more potent sensual pleasures, that clear and reasoned thought plays very little part in their life.

On the other hand, by developing our powers of mental awareness, discrimination and will, and by cultivating the sensitivity of our responses to stimuli, we may so order matters that we remain in complete control of our emotions, thoughts and actions, undisturbed by desires, events or circumstances. The first step in this direction is to make ourselves aware of our body in all its parts and functions. Most of our thoughts and actions are carried out below the conscious level. This is necessary to a certain extent, for the mind can only hold one thing at a time, and would break down if it were called upon to exercise conscious control over all the many functions of the organs, nerves and muscles of the body simultaneously. The mind therefore has its different component parts to deal with these functions, but more of this in our next chapter, in which the mental aspects will be dealt with.

By concentrating the mind upon a particular function or organ, we become aware of it, we bring it into the focus of the conscious part of mind. By then exercising a conscious physical effort upon the part or organ, energy is directed to it. If this process is repeated at given intervals for a period, that part or organ becomes more sensitive, and more responsive to the command of will. In this manner, weakness is turned into strength, deficient organs, muscles and glands are built up to peak condition and are maintained as such, and a healthy body is ours.

This is the principle upon which Hatha Yoga operates. When asanas and postures are performed, a full effort of consciousness is used in which energy is directed to that part being worked upon. Hatha Yoga insists that positive thought must always accompany exercise, or it will be of little value. A picture must be held in the mind of the perfect ideal of that which we are trying to achieve, whether it be a healthy liver, powerful lungs, strong muscles, or whatever. In time, the mental image becomes reality, that which is held in the mind clearly and in strength, will in time become manifested in the physical. This is simply cause and effect, in which mind operates upon energy, directing it through existing natural laws of chemical exchange to growth of matter.

In this brief survey much has had to be omitted, for to cover the whole philosophy of Hatha Yoga would take several volumes. But there is one other point of major importance to our study which must be included. This is the body system known as the Endocrine Glands. These are among the most important in the body, having an immediate effect upon health, growth and mental condition; in particular upon personality. These glands function by passing internal secretions directly into the bloodsteam, in which they reflect a difference to those other organs which pass their secretions externally through ducts, such as the bile, which passes from the liver in the "bile duct". Because of this action peculiar to themselves, the endocrine glands are referred to as "ductless", and the endocrine system as the "ductless system". The positions of the endocrine glands are indicated in Fig. 9 whilst Fig. 8b shows the "Shoulder Stand" asana and Fig. 10, the "Plough", which have been designed with particular consideration for maintaining these glands in supple and efficient condition.

Fig. 8b

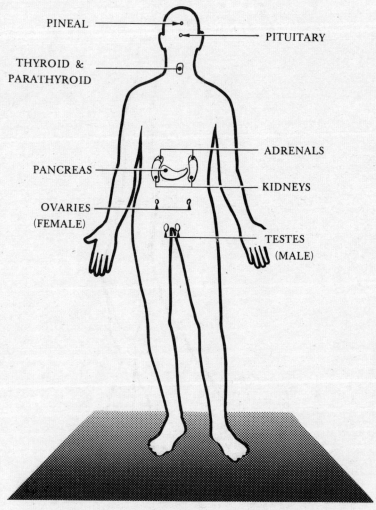

Fig. 9 The ductless glands (endocrine system)

Fig. 10

The ductless glands consist of the ovaries and the testes, the adrenals and suprarenals, thyroid and parathyroid, pituitary and pineal (though mention must be made of the fact that some glands, such as the testes, function both internally and externally). The proper functioning of these glands is vital to the body's health, in particular to the nervous system, so that a weakness or a malfunctioning of any of the ductless glands is immediately reflected in depression, lassitude, nervous tension and irritability. If such a condition is allowed to continue, then permanent mental and/or physical damage can result. We have seen that the body relies upon the nourishment and replacement of cells for its continued health and efficiency. If the endocrine system is inefficient or inadequate, however, then the anabolic process of assimilation, nourishment and repair of cells becomes impaired, and the catabolic process of wastage of cells proceeds at a rate greater than that of anabolism. This results in degeneration of body structure and muscle power. It is, in fact, what is known as the "ageing process".

In addition to the bodily development brought about by the combined effects of Hatha Yoga physical exercises and their mental counterparts, the effects of Yama and Niyama are also complementary, with particular reference to their effects upon the endocrine system, by assisting in the establishment of that psycho-somatic harmony which is essential for health and peace of mind. The Bhagavad Gita tells us that the emotions of love, anger and greed are destructive forces which militate against spiritual growth; they also militate against health. Negative emotions such as those mentioned, to which we may add jealousy, hatred, fear and so on, have an adverse effect upon the glands and the body organs. If these emotions are given free rein and are allowed to repeat themselves with any frequency (that is if they become habitual), tissues can be permanently damaged, and glands malfunction.

To illustrate this point, let us take for example the effect of shock. This is known to kill if sufficiently powerful, its action being to paralyse the nerves so that muscular action temporarily ceases and heart and brain cannot function. If the latter state continues for only a short time, then death results. During the last war, many cases of diabetes were found to be due to shock following bombing raids. A state of anxiety or frustration if allowed to continue, will adversely affect the endocrine glands, causing permanent ageing of the body, which is only too visible in wrinkled skin and greying hair. Too much adrenalin caused by anger or fear, will raise the blood pressure, again resulting in damage to tissue and organs. A prolonged condition of depression can result in premature and permanent ageing, as this affects the thyroid gland. Furthermore, as the thyroid is one of the body's principal guardians against toxic elements, disease can be the result of an inefficient thyroid. Shock has also been known to affect the sexual glands, whilst even simple embarrassment can cause impotence, temporary or permanent.

So far we have spoken only of the negative emotions, with their damaging, corrosive effects. Fortunately there are also positive emotions which assist health and well-being. Confidence is an attitude of mind to be cultivated assiduously. Hope is born of Faith, their mutually strong, positive forces having an uplifting and strengthening effect upon the whole system. Relaxation, combined with mental attitudes of hope and confidence, will release taut nerves and muscles, allowing the whole mechanism of the body to operate freely and in harmony, as nature intended.

"Sarvangasana", the so-called "death pose", is a most valuable aid to relaxation, in which the body takes up a prone position upon the floor, lying upon the back, the mind being then focused on each muscle in turn from toe to top, ordering and sensing complete relaxation. This is followed by holding in the mind a picture of peaceful calm, of something with pleasant associations, so that the entire system, physical and mental, feels the tension melting away, the mind slipping smoothly into a deep calm. Practised for only 15 minutes each day or during a time of particular stress, this asana is of the utmost value. It helps in cases of backache and fatigue, and if in the latter case one concentrates on deep, rhythmic breathing, visualising at the same an intake of Prana, this also can be most invigorating and refreshing.

It is clear, then, that attention to the nervous system is of fundamental importance. Also this is so closely involved with the function of mind, that the two must be considered as integral parts of a common function. We know too that thought precedes action, so that the first approach to control is through the mind by controlling one's thoughts, whilst thought, in turn, is the result of a mental attitude. Therefore it becomes evident that the entire process of obtaining and maintaining health must begin with a sincere examination of our mental attitudes and patterns of thought. The abstentions and observances of Yama and Niyama respectively are adequate guides to moral attitudes and behaviour, so that if one adheres to these, one can be assured of looking in the right direction.

Summarising the value of Hatha Yoga, we may now say that, if for a consistent effort of no more than twenty minutes each day, one may be assured of a healthy body, strong in all its parts, erect, supple, athletic, of the right weight, increased in vitality and stamina, with strong, well-formed muscles, graceful carriage, mental and physical buoyancy, a strong will, optimism, increased powers of observation and concentration, a feeling of "one-ness" with all beings, and a sense of belonging.

Hatha Yoga has been called the world's finest system of physical culture, but it has also the additional advantages that it calls for no adherence to any particular sect or dogma, can be practised by anyone of any age, requires no specialised apparatus, and can be performed in the small space required by the body in a standing or lying position.

The rewards of perseverance are great and far outweigh the expenditure of a little time and energy, but the physical and mental advantages outlined, great though they be, are only the first steps on the ladder of Self Realisation, the true Yoga which is Spiritual Union. Without these first steps, however, progress to the advanced mental and spiritual training would be impossible, for as we said at the outset of this chapter, the first step in Yoga is Purification.

CHAPTER 8

The Mental Approach – Raja and Jnana Yoga

In the previous chapter we took a brief look at the evolution of man's physical structure, and we saw how, behind all life, there is a powerful force which urges every living thing towards a greater degree of mobility, awareness and perfection, a "real"-isation of the ideal. We have also seen that this driving force, which we called the "Creative Will", is inherent in every form of life. But mankind is unique in being possessed, not only of this driving force, but also of a conscious awareness of his environment and of himself. He is not, alas, very often conscious of the powerful forces within himself. He has intelligence, allied to the power of reason, however, and a will by which he may act of his own volition upon decisions made by himself. So we come to the conclusion that it is largely within the power of man himself to control whatever may happen to him from the objective, external world, whilst his reaction to such events are individualised by personal experience, under-standing, training and will.

Hatha Yoga teaches all one needs to know about personal biology; how to keep fit and strong, and how to attain healthy longevity. In its more advanced practices, however, Hatha Yoga enters the psychic sphere, teaching how, by purification, intense concentration, adherence to diet combined with physical and mental exercises, the psychic barriers may be broken, and one can dwell at will in the world of the Spirit in a state of full consciousness. This is the ultimate goal of all Yoga, the various Schools are but different paths by which it may be reached.

Apart from the health-giving benefits and the material rewards of Hatha Yoga, it is of the greatest importance that the student recognise the full implications of body-mind relationship and the mechanism by which this operates, that actions or conditions in the one have a corresponding effect upon the other. When full knowledge of the wonderful mechanism of the body has been attained, and also an understanding of the functions of mind at its various levels (the instinctive, sub-conscious, conscious and super-conscious), imagination and concentration may be brought into play, directing the powers of Creative Will to develop both mind and body to the ideal.

It must be emphasised that an essential part of the process of "realisation" is the holding in the mind of a clearly defined image of what we wish to attain. How can one hope to bring into concrete form, something which is vague and nebulous in the mind? Unless our ideas are clear and our thoughts constructive and positive there is little hope of success, but with a trained intelligence and perseverance, the force of Will can be brought to operate upon the subtle substance of mind (Chitta), to crystallise the subtle into material form. It is self-evident that a well-developed imagination is an essential tool, and one must use every opportunity to develop this power.

This is the essence of "mind over matter".

As awareness develops, one becomes conscious of the existence of a wider sphere of activities as the boundaries of knowledge and experience are extended. As the process of learning continues, one becomes ever more aware that our universe is controlled by a system of immutable and inflexible laws. Every single thing in this universe is subject to those laws of force and energy which regulate it. The Laws of Physics, Chemistry, Dynamics, Statics, Biology, Electricity, the natural laws of growth and decay, birth and death, the four seasons of the year, the motion of the planets, all are part of a cosmic whole. By sheer intelligence and diligence plus courage and determination, man is uncovering one by one the secrets of the universe, breaking down those barriers which exist between the physical world, the laws which govern it, and finally, the controlling influence behind it all.

With each new discovery, understanding grows and a new step forward is taken as man's consciousness expands to absorb the new knowledge. As new physical laws are discovered, so man's inner nature grows to that extent, reaching out to build the new concepts into his being. His mental capacities are thereby extended, developing new patterns of thought and wider horizons, as yet another way is found by which environment can be overcome, or natural laws made use of to bring mankind another step closer to the ideal. But history has proved this process to be arduous, painful, costly and slow. Costly in lives and in the expenditure of the world's natural resources and wealth, and, excepting the current period, slow in making its impact.

Yogi philosophy states that all knowledge already exists within man himself, and can be found by simply following the inner path to the Spirit. Whence comes inspiration? Certainly not from an external source; this can only be the stimuli which releases it. Whence comes the illumination of revelation or the power of genius? Again we must admit, not from any external source. Some of man's greatest discoveries have been made through flashes of intuition which enter the consciousness from some source which has the power to illuminate the mind to a point which could not be reached by reasoned argument or logical thought.

It is the task of Raja Yoga to carry mankind into that realm of mind which is the home and the source of inspiration. In following the inner path to the Spirit, to that ultimate consciousness in which the "One" is experienced, man may absorb in a moment those secrets of nature for which so much has been sacrificed in the past. Patience, Practice and Perseverance are the vehicles on which man must travel. Let us now learn the Way.

It should be clear that progress into the world of mind, and from thence into the world of Spirit, is a matter of personal refinement and adjustment. Until the dross has been separated from the ore, the gold will remain in bondage. Until one learns to recognise gross matter for what it really is, and how the gross matter comprising the human body may be refined by the methods taught in Hatha Yoga, the finer vibrations from the sphere of ethereal matter cannot penetrate man's consciousness, can make no impact upon human perceptions.

To look at this from a different aspect, we may take as an example an object which is being photographed. If we use an ordinary camera, then the resulting photograph would show an image almost identical to the image projected to the brain through our own vision. If we then fitted a filter over the lens of the camera so that light waves of a certain frequency only were admitted, the second photograph would look quite different from the first, and we would then have quite a different impression of the object being photographed. Although the general outline may remain the same, the texture and general character of the object would appear to have changed. An X-ray photograph may be taken as a further example, in which a solid body appears as a nebulous, translucent shape.

It is a fact that the sum total of the mechanism of our sensory perceptions is able to function only within a narrow band of about one ninth of the total scale of physical vibrations. This means that we can only be aware of one ninth of the total phenomena taking place in the world about us, the remaining eight ninths being beyond the range of our perceptions. Even the use of scientific instruments increases the range only marginally. Clearly, if we were able to adjust our "frequencies" at will, we would be able to perceive a world of far greater complexity and wider dimension than the world of solid forms with which we are familiar. Our sensory limitations even keep us in ignorance of the vast majority of what is happening in our own physical dimension. If you look at Fig. 11 and study it well, you will observe from the left-hand column that our senses can only perceive vibrations within narrow limits (or wave-bands). If these are related mathematically to the total known energy range, it will be found that our physical sense perceptions can apprehend no more than one thousand millionth part of the total possible range.

Some fortunate people are naturally gifted with an extended range of perception. They can both see and hear beyond the normal physical range, and into this category come the clairvoyants, clairaudients, telepathy, psychometry, telekinesis.

In the practice of Yoga we increase our range of vibrations so that we may become attuned to the vibrations of the subtle world. Each individual may then become a channel through which may flow the knowledge, the strength and the power of the Spirit.

One can now begin to see the careful reasoning and planning behind the training of Yoga, and how this may lead, through purification study and practice, to sensory control and a refinement, first of body, then of mind, by which perceptions may be raised to a higher level, and understanding to a higher plane.

The need for dietary control is self-evident, for we "become what we eat", so that heavy foods, spicy foods, alcohol, tobacco and drugs, only increase the bondage of the body to matter and to the lower orders, whilst excitement, pleasures, emotions and worry, divert mental energy into channels of useless wastage, unproductive, and binding to a path of frustration and disappointment, instead of to that expansion and peace of mind, that freedom, which we all desire.

Yama and Niyama, the observances and abstentions which are the first of the Eight Limbs of Yoga, are clearly essential for developing the right pattern of behaviour and thought, as we discussed in our earlier chapters. One can see also the reasoned guidance behind the Ten Commandments of Christianity and for asceticism in religious orders. In the latter respect, however, Yoga is careful to stipulate that extremes in either direction are wrong, as they tend only to defeat their object by attracting the attention away from the real reason for the exercise. The Gita instructs that, "This Yoga is not for him who eats too much or sleeps too much, nor is it for him who gives up sleep and food. To him who is temperate in eating and recreation, who is restrained in his actions, whose sleeping and waking are regulated, Yoga is the destroyer of misery. (6–16/17)."

"Moderation in all things" may be a well-worn cliché, but it is also sound advice, although of course, one must beware of living in a state of permanent neutrality in which one achieves nothing at all and life becomes fruitless.

The third of the Eight Limbs of Yoga is "Asana", whose effects in strengthening and refining the body we have already discussed. But every force in the physical world has its reflected counterpart in the subtle, so that Asanas have the double effect of developing simultaneously both the physical and subtle bodies, so long as the power of mind be properly applied in sympathy with the physical effort. These three, Yama, Niyama and Asana, although perhaps more proper to the study of Hatha Yoga, provide also an essential preliminary to Raja Yoga. Indeed, they are fundamental to Yoga in all its different forms.

The remaining five Limbs bring us into the sphere of Raja Yoga, and these we will now investigate. Taking them in the order in which they must be approached, these five Limbs are, Pranayama, Pratyahara, Dharana, Dhyana and Samadhi.

The first of these, Pranayama, is also met with in Hatha Yoga

Fig. 11. The spectrum of electro-magnetic energy

Physical sense perception	Wavelength (Metres)	Frequency Cycles/sec.
	$3 \cdot 10^7$	10
	$3 \cdot 10^6$	10^2
Hearing	$3 \cdot 10^5$	10^3
	$3 \cdot 10^4$	10^4
	$3 \cdot 10^3$	10^5
	$3 \cdot 10^2$	10^6
	$3 \cdot 10$	10^7
	$3 \cdot 1$	10^8
	$3 \cdot 10^{-1}$	10^9
	$3 \cdot 10^{-2}$	10^{10}
	$3 \cdot 10^{-3}$	10^{11}
Touch — Taste and Smell	$3 \cdot 10^{-4}$	10^{12}
	$3 \cdot 10^{-5}$	10^{13}
	$3 \cdot 10^{-6}$	10^{14}
Sight	$3 \cdot 10^{-7}$	10^{15}
	$3 \cdot 10^{-8}$	10^{16}
	$3 \cdot 10^{-9}$	10^{17}
	$3 \cdot 10^{-10}$	10^{18}
	$3 \cdot 10^{-11}$	10^{19}
	$3 \cdot 10^{-12}$	10^{20}
	$3 \cdot 10^{-13}$	10^{21}
	$3 \cdot 10^{-14}$	10^{22}
	$3 \cdot 10^{-15}$	10^{23}
	$3 \cdot 10^{-16}$	10^{24}

Notes:
Energy increases as frequency rises
according to the Law of Energy where
energy $= h \times v$

$v =$ frequency in cycles per second
$h =$ Planck's constant
$= 6 \cdot 624 \times 10^{-27}$ erg/secs

Scientific classification	Use	Construction of matter
Low frequency	Electricity supply	Physical sense-perception uses only a one-thousand millionth part of the known energy range
Audio-frequency	Telephones, tape recorders, etc.	
Long wave H.F.		
Medium wave H.F.	Radio	
Short wave H.F.		
Ultra-short wave	Television	
Ultra-high frequency	Radar	
Heat and Infra-red	Various means of heating	Vibration of molecules
		Outer shell Electron emission – the building of molecules
Visible light		
Ultra-violet	Studies of molecular construction of matter	Vibration of atoms Inner shell electron emission – involved in building molecules of the lightest elements
X-rays		
α-radiation	Studies of construction of the atom	
Cosmic radiation		

...uencies up to that of visible light
...he limit of Sense-Perception.
...gher frequencies, Mass, Space,
...Time are meaningless. These
...er energies can only be measured
...egradation in Matter.

PREPARED BY JOHN W. ANTWIS

in its elementary form, but whereas in Hatha the emphasis is upon the physical effects, in particular the special breathing practices, in Raja Yoga the teaching moves into the subtle world, the world of mind, where Pranayama takes on a deeper meaning and the breathing practices lead inward from the physical to the subtle. The word itself means "control of Prana"; it is not simply the "control of breath", and herein lies its deeper significance. What, then, is this Prana which we have to learn to control, and what are its effects?

To answer these questions we must begin with an analysis of matter itself, and follow this by an analysis of those senses by which we perceive the phenomena of matter and the world about us.

The philosophy of the Upanishads tells us that all matter, whether in the world of the physical, mental or subtle, is basically of the one same essence. Its state is said to differ only according to the degree of its refinement, its density, or its natural rate of vibration. This basic substance or entity is called "Akasa" in the Sanskrit. It is held to permeate the entire universe and all it contains. Akasa is said to take form on being acted upon by the force of Prana, Prana being the absolute essence of all the energy and power of the universe, in the same way in which Akasa is the essence of all substance. We therefore have these two fundamental entities, Akasa and Prana, which are the absolutes of all matter and power respectively, the action of the one upon the other causing a compression or crystallisation to take place, so creating those forms which are familiar to our physical perceptions.

If we wish to analyse our physical world, we may begin by stating the known facts that all matter is composed of atoms, and that the atoms are forms of electrical charges, concentrated into "vortices of energy" which are known as protons, electrons and neutrons. Remembering that Akasa is the fundamental essence of all substance in all spheres, one can now visualise the action of the Pranic force, concentrating the Akasa to form the particles of the atom. The manner in which these particles are assembled determines the nature and character of the substance so formed, and man has now analysed these and assembled them into the table of atomic weights and numbers with which every schoolboy is now familiar, and in which appears the atomic analysis of every substance known to man.

The subtle essence, Akasa, is too fine to be apprehended by normal sense perception, as also is the fundamental of force, Prana. Neither can these be perceived by the instruments of science, which can only measure effects, they cannot yet penetrate into the subtle world, and so far can extend only the fringes of our own senses. These elements could be perceived by our own senses, however, if our senses were sufficiently refined to become sensitive to them. It is simply a matter of purifying and refining the physical senses until they may become attuned to the finer vibrations. All forms of matter are compounded of these two, Akasa and Prana, so it is finally to the vibrations of these two essences that we must become attuned. We must begin at the point at which we find ourselves, so that to trace Akasa to its finer limits we must begin with its gross manifestation which is matter, and to trace Prana we must approach it through its manifestations as the forces which we know, namely, gravity, electro-magnetism, and all applied forces whose laws have been established through the process of analysing their effects.

A moment's thought on the foregoing will reveal the structure of the physical, mental and even the spiritual worlds, as being planes of existence which differ only in terms of density and substance. The whole range of existence can be seen as a continuing series of decreasing vibrations, one "band of vibrations" being imperceptible to the others by reason of the limitations of the perceptive faculties within that range. It is the task of Yoga, and indeed of all religion, to raise our perceptions to that higher level which is the world of the Spirit, in which we already dwell as our Real Self.

A simple illustration of the idea can be found in Fig. 12, in which Fig. 12(b) represents the composition of white light, which, as we know, if passed through a prism of glass, becomes broken up into its constituent colours. These colours derive their difference solely by their differences in wavelength, and reference to the left-hand column of Fig. 11 will illustrate just how limited our range of vision is, when compared to the overall spectrum.

In Fig. 12(b) we see the single ray of light divided into many. Fig. 12(a) is an analogy between the division of the one ray into many, and the philosophic mystery known as "The One and the Many". In the diagram is pictured symbolically the manner in which the Power of The One (The One Creator) generates the

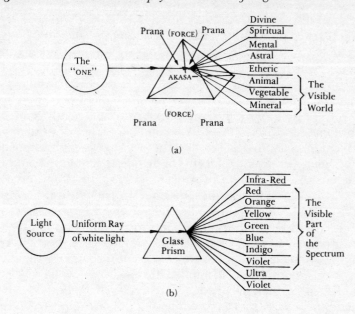

Fig. 12

ultimate essence of matter which we now know as Akasa, and how Pranic energy acts upon that ultimate essence to create several spheres of existence, varying only in degree of density and vibration, from the Divine to the lowest form of matter. In this can also be seen the process of involution of the Spirit, and furthermore, how the withdrawal of Divine Power would result in complete and instantaneous dissolution of the universe and all that it contains.

Life on the different planes therefore appears merely as different states of vibration. Evolution has so far endowed man with perceptions which can only apprehend a very limited range of vibrations existing in his own physical sphere, but God has also endowed him with intelligence and will, so that he may refine himself by his own activities, to a higher, happier and more complete state of "Being".

Now Prana is also that living force which activates the nervous system of the body. It is also the force by which mind operates upon Chitta (the mind-stuff), to formulate images and thought-patterns; it is the dynamic, motivating force of thought, and it is at this point that Pranayama moves from simple control of breath into the world of mind. It is at this point that one begins to perceive how, in beginning with the simple control of breath, and from thence to the control of mind, one can ultimately achieve the power to command Prana and the basic life forces of the universe, and if one finally achieves the peak of Adeptship, of controlling matter and form.

The aim of Pranayama is therefore nothing less than this, to attain control of the forces of nature, matter and mind.

You may feel this to be an overstatement, a mere extrapolation of an hypothesis. This is not so. Verification can easily be found in the history of the Yogis of India and Tibet and in their biographies. (For example *The Autobiography of a Yogi* by Yogananda published by Rider & Co.) Even though the true Yogi Adept is extremely difficult to find, there exists ample written evidence by reliable eyewitnesses of phenomena produced by Adepts, sufficiently super-normal to be labelled "miraculous". The basic teaching of such practices has existed for thousands of years in the sacred books of India, the Vedas and the Upanishads.

Our greatest difficulty nowadays lies in the fact that we have lived immersed in materialism and the western way of life for so many generations, that contact with the subtle worlds of mind and spirit have become so attenuated as to be almost non-existent. It is now man's task to realise, individually, where the true Reality lies, what is man's true nature, and to turn his aspirations in that direction.

The Katha Upanishad gives a clear direction in this respect, when it says, "The Creative Self formed the eyes to see objects outside itself and the ears to hear sounds outside itself. All the senses are created to perceive objects outside the Self. They go to the world of matter and form which exists outside the Real Self, not to the true world of the Self within. But few sages have turned their senses inwards in their burning desire for freedom and immortality, and they alone have seen the Self."

In the Tantric teaching of Tibetan Yoga, we find another aspect of the same thought. It is taught that man's intelligence is free to decide into which sphere his consciousness may be directed, either to the external world of matter, or to the inner world of Spirit. The Upanishad teaches the possibility of man's ability to reverse the normal direction of sense perception, from external objectivity to internal perception, whereby he may apprehend the action of the subtle life forces which move within himself, and then to follow them to their source of origin in the subtle world. In Tibetan Yoga this action is called, "the turning about in the seat of deepest consciousness", about which we shall have more to say later.

We may now follow the Eight Limbs of Yoga as they move into deeper territory. We know that the essence of matter is a combination of Akasa and Prana, and we have learnt that Prana is the basic energy of the universe, the life force which is fundamental to all living things. We must now learn how Prana may be apprehended and controlled.

It is obvious that we cannot hope to leap immediately into a position of control, for, as in all things, perfection can only come with teaching, training and perseverance in application. It is also obvious that one must begin with the physical and mental apparatus with which one has been endowed. The first step is therefore to work upon these with the knowledge of what they are, what they may become, and how the ideal may be achieved. In other words we must begin with what we have. Furthermore, no two people begin at exactly the same point; no two people have identical needs, and herein lies the incalculable value of a personal teacher, who is able to analyse the needs of the individual, and is able to direct him accordingly.

However, a Self-realised Guru being almost impossible to find in the West, the western student must apply his trained intelligence and his own inner voice to be his guide. The next step in Pranayama is the introspective self-analysis of the student by himself. Hatha Yoga will have taught him his bodily functions in the physical sense, he must now trace these to their point of origin. The practices of concentration and meditation taught by Raja Yoga are now brought into operation, and action of Prana is traced from its manifestation in the physical functions, to an apprehension of Prana itself. The student now learns to direct his attention, and to focus his concentration, upon his own organic activities, learning to recognise the sounds and motions taking place in his various parts, and finally attuning himself to the finer vibrations of those life forces which flow throughout the body, which are in fact the life currents of Prana.

In Hatha Yoga we learn to control the motion of the lungs, establishing a pattern of rhythmic breathing related to the pulse-beats of the heart. Having so established this rhythm that it has become automatic, attention is then to be directed to the inner path taken by the breath, the ear being attuned to the fine vibrations thereby generated. When lung motion has been successfully brought under control, then other and even finer motions may be apprehended.

If the mind is concentrated upon a point, then awareness is increased so that perception of activity at that point becomes more acute. In this manner, concentration upon the motions and sensations involved in the act of breathing, will bring an awareness of the subtle vibrations in that area.

"Seeing is believing", or to put it more succinctly, to experience a thing is to know it, and mere belief is left behind in the true knowledge which follows experience. We may be told a thing and may be convinced of its truth, but if we have personally experienced that thing, then that experience becomes a part of ourself and we know in our inner self of its truth. Belief can never replace true knowledge, so it is incumbent upon us to undergo experience in order that we may learn truly. One may read a thousand books and believe, but the smallest grain of experience is the better teacher. Books are, of course, essential in the first place to give us the necessary guidance, but this must be followed by personal effort and experience, or all the reading will be without value.

Therefore, to prove what has been said, and to obtain that personal experience which turns belief into knowledge, here is a small experiment. Concentrate attention upon the tip of the nose for a short time each day (using the same time of day each time if possible), after some time (depending upon the individual), subtle perfumes will be experienced, although nothing physical exists to generate the scent. Apply this simple experiment if you will, so that from this one particularisation of the general principle, confidence will be established in the generalisation.

By extending such experiments in concentration to different parts of the body, the mind will become sufficiently developed to move deeper into the bodily functions; when lung motion has been mastered and the life current therein apprehended, then the next step is the apprehension and control of the currents and

forces in the nervous system. The finer sounds and movements
of the nerve currents are also generated by Prana, and having
gained experience by following the path of the breath, we may
now become aware of the action of Prana in other parts of the
body.

The nerve centre which regulates breathing has also a
controlling effect upon the entire bodily system of nerve
currents, so that our next step must be to listen for the
movement of the nerve currents as they flow through the body.
Much has been written in the Upanishads on this subject, from
which it becomes evident that concentration upon the area of
the heart is of the greatest importance, for herein lies the core of
man's being. As the centre of the highest spiritual emotion, the
heart is the seat of the force of Love, wherein is established a link
with that which is Divine. In all forms of Yoga, the heart is given
as a principal point for meditation. In Tantric Yoga, the Heart
Centre (Chakra), is associated with the element of fire. By this is
meant the fire of inspiration and devotion, not the earthly fire of
combustion. Concentration on the Heart Centre will bring one
closer to Divine Love, and is of the greatest value in achieving
that refinement which extends perception, achieving that degree
of sensitivity by which one may become aware of higher planes
of existence. To live jointly and consciously upon the higher
planes and upon our physical plane is the ultimate goal of Yoga.

Control of breathing again becomes a necessity when we
approach the study of concentration, for as has already been
said, by controlling lung motion we establish a parallel, or
sympathetic control of those nerve centres which, in their turn,
control other parts of the body. Furthermore, by slowing down
the rate of breathing, we can simultaneously slow down the
process of thought, so assisting in bringing the mind itself under
control.

The method of establishing rhythmic breathing is given in my
previous book (*Yoga The Key to Life*; see "Kapala Bati", page 51,
and "Rhythmic Breathing", page 93), to which the reader is
referred. The exercises should be practised in conjunction with
the exercises in concentration also given in that book.

The practice of Brahmacharya ("Chastity", op. cit., page
102), goes essentially with the practice of concentration, for to
dissipate sexual energy is to dissipate the life force itself. The
primary effect of such dissipation is an immediate weakening of

the mental forces, resulting in loss of concentration, listlessness and irritability; attention wanders, judgement is impaired, and the brain becomes dull. Any attempt to achieve mental powers or control of mind is quite useless unless chastity is observed. Indeed, the additional strain put upon the system by attempting Yogic practices whilst at the same time indulging in an unchaste life and the satisfaction of appetites, will lead undoubtedly to a nervous breakdown. Jesus taught that, "As a man thinks in his heart, so is he". Chastity, therefore, must begin in the mind, so that by control of thought, emotion and desire may also be controlled. Thought always precedes action, so that if the thought be killed, or the mind be so trained that no unwanted thought will arise, then no action can follow and we are freed from an unhappy chain of cause and effect.

The next of the Eight Limbs is Pratyahara, and this we must now consider; it is the Fifth Limb of Yoga. The literal meaning of Pratyahara is "drawing together", or "gathering". In this case it is a gathering of the mental forces, a collection of the power of thought to one central point, from which thought will always tend to stray. The aim, however, is to control, not only thought, but also the experience of sensation. Let us take a brief look at the mechanism of sensation, from which we may observe how sensation may be controlled.

We have already seen how our senses are organised to react to stimuli directed to them from an external source. The eyes, for example, receive the light rays which are reflected from an object, passing the impulses so generated to their own special reception centre in the brain. Now if a person were to die suddenly, at the very moment of looking at an object, the eyes remaining open, the same light rays would impinge on the retina of the eyes, but there would no longer be any consciousness of the fact. Everything would be exactly the same as before, except for the absence of the act of "seeing". The same thing would apply also to all the other senses, for although the stimuli would still be there and the organs of sense unchanged, consciousness of the stimuli would have gone.

Suppose that you had just come in from the cold, and walk over to the fire for a moment, holding your hands to the blaze to feel the warmth. All your consciousness is concentrated for the moment upon the sensation of warmth, so that for the moment you are unaware of the message being relayed to the brain by your other senses. Perhaps there is a clock ticking, or the quiet sound of soft music playing on the radio; perhaps you have even left the door open so that there is a draught. But your attention is concentrated upon the heat playing upon your hands, and for the moment the messages of your other senses go unheeded, you are quite unaware of them. Then, perhaps, you sit in your favourite armchair, pick up the newspaper and begin to read. Immediately your attention becomes focused upon the newsprint, your consciousness of the sensation of warmth on your hands will disappear, you are only aware of the print. Perhaps, then, a particularly loud passage of music attracts your attention to the radio, and for a while you become conscious only of the music, both warmth and newspaper disappear from the field of consciousness.

Such a sequence of events gives a clue to the mechanism of sense perception, for it is evident that, although the organs of perception are receiving impressions all the time and are passing their impulses to the brain, the message is accepted only from that organ to which attention, and so consciousness, has been directed. In other words, consciousness of sensation can only take place when the mind has been directed to a particular organ, and the process of perception can therefore be seen as a sequence of events whereby stimuli from external objects impinge upon the organs of perception, the function of that organ then being controlled by its own particular centre in the brain. Mind being joined to that organ, sensory perception then takes place in which the object of the stimulus is transmitted in image to our consciousness. It is then the work of the intelligence to interpret the message so received, and to direct, via the brain, an impulse which moves in the opposite direction to the impulse of the stimulus, which then activates the motor nerves into operation of muscles, so performing whatever action that "manas" has considered to be necessary.

The importance of understanding the mechanism of perception lies, not only in appreciation of the sequence of events just described, but in the realisation that the process can be inhibited by control. In other words, inasmuch as perception occurs when the mind is directed to a particular organ of perception, so can this perception (and so sensation) be blocked from the consciousness by withdrawing the mind from that organ. This is, in fact, what happens in hypnosis, when a person is rendered unable to react to normal sensation, the mind of the subject having been withdrawn under control of the hypnotist. The same process can be achieved by the individual upon himself, in the process known as self-hypnosis.

This is also the essence of Pratyahara. We have said that the literal meaning of the word is a "drawing together". It can now be seen that the first step in the process is a withdrawal of the mind from the organs of perception. It is a drawing away of the mind from external objects so that it may be turned inward in meditation.

One of the principal reasons for the ascetic's withdrawal from the world, is to reduce and control the flow of sensations which impinge in unending stream upon our senses in the work-a-day world. Even in normal life we are impelled to exercise some control over our sensory perceptions, or we would soon become nervous wrecks. We can all recall a walk down some high street, during which our senses have been bombarded from many different sources. The strongest of these, and the one which is most likely to cause us distress, is noise. Noise from buses, cars, motor-cycles, hooters, radios, pneumatic drills, jet propelled aeroplanes, all project their pressures upon the ear.

Simultaneously, our eyes are subjected to a variety of stimuli from things both moving and stationary. In traffic one must judge speed and distance instantaneously on peril of our lives. We must take cognisance of signals and signs, whether we be pedestrian or motorist. Flashing neon signs call our attention to advertisements, notices in shop windows, done in lurid, fluorescent paints, draw our eyes in another direction, whilst we still have to watch where we are going, or collide with someone or something.

At the same time our skin is being acted upon by the air, and has the sensation of heat or cold, relaying the message to the controlling centre in the brain which maintains our body at the correct temperature. Perhaps in the middle of all this we feel the sensation of hunger and a desire for food.

So it is that, whether we like it or not, and whether we are conscious of it or not, we are being continually bombarded by a mass of various stimuli from both external and internal sources, and by virtue of the fact that we can only be conscious of one of these sensations at any one moment of time, we are automatically, if unconsciously, practising sense withdrawal from all those organs of which we are unconscious. Sense-control, therefore, can be seen as a perfectly natural process (and one which is most necessary today). Once we are aware of the mechanism of the process, it is only a matter of practice as to what degree of withdrawal and control we are able to achieve.

It is also evident that practice to any degree cannot take place in ordinary environment. We must choose a place which is, or can be made, remote from disturbance of sound or interruption, moving things, people, changes of temperature, and any other form of distraction. Herein lies the value of withdrawal from the world, be it only for short periods at given intervals, such as those "Retreats" practised by Christian communities, now, happily, available to the laity as well as to the enclosed religious. The benefit of such withdrawal is not only spiritual, it also provides a splendid tonic for over-tired nerves.

After Pratyahara comes Dharana, a further stage in control in which the mind becomes "one-pointed", is held at one point or to one thing without deviation. Having withheld the senses in the process of Pratyahara, the will must then be exerted to hold the mind steadily in concentration upon one thing or point. Under normal conditions the mind is a kaleidoscope of movement, one thought following upon another as attention drifts from one attraction to another. The control of attention is therefore the first thing we must learn, and when attention is held the mind is concentrated upon that particular subject in greater and greater detail, until the mind is completely absorbed in the subject. This is the preliminary to Dharana, and as a preparatory exercise, a Guru will often instruct his Chela to concentrate his attention upon one particular spot of his body. If, for example, the attention is concentrated upon a particular spot on the hand, first its general topography is considered, its shape, the appearance of the skin, the disposition and colouring of the veins, and so on. Attention is then focused upon a small section, say in the centre of the back of the hand, and the mind is then concentrated and held to this point. The aim is for the student to hold his attention without wavering, to this point, noting the number of times his mind wanders away, and trying to increase the length of time the mind can be held to the point without deviation.

Having practised upon such an external object, and achieved some degree of control, the mind is then directed inwardly to inner parts and organs of the body, the heart being the organ most generally favoured as we have seen.

Dharana having been mastered, the next step is the Seventh Limb of Yoga, Dhyana, which is the practice of meditation. Once the mind can be held unwaveringly to a particular point, then there comes an unbroken contact with the object of meditation, with a continuous flow of thought about that object only. This stage is called Dhyana, upon which we will say more in our next chapter.

The final stage, the Eighth Limb of Yoga, is Samadhi, the peak and final goal of all Yogic practices. Dhyana having been established and a continuous link created with the object of meditation, complete absorption then occurs in which the subject and object become one. Although these final three stages must be approached and mastered singly and in the right order, the process is really one continuous sequence of events. The first step is Dharana in which the art of concentration is mastered, the second is Dhyana in which one attains a continuous and unbroken flow of thought about the object of meditation and thus gains knowledge and insight about it, and finally, meditation flows into union with the object, that union which is the true Yoga, and the state of Samadhi is attained. These three, Dharana, Dhyana and Samadhi are called collectively, "Samyama".

The value of Raja Yoga now becomes clear, for if we wish only to improve our mental powers of concentration, then Raja Yoga will accomplish this for us, but if our aims are high and we seek union with the Divine, then Raja Yoga is the path by which this may be attained.

CHAPTER 9

Consciousness, Prayer and Meditation

Consciousness is a word which is given many meanings. In general it is used to indicate what is going on around and inside us. It differs considerably in degree according to the individual. Consciousness must not be confused with intelligence, for we have seen in our earlier work (*Yoga The Key to Life*, page 21), that even in the mineral world there exists an intelligence which can be recognised in the formation and growth of crystals.

The awareness, or consciousness, with which we are concerned, is arrived at between the fifth and sixth Principles of Man, as described previously (op. cit., page 16). Spiritual Mind operates upon Intellect, in the functional area of Manas.

The Manduka Upanishad (op. cit., page 139) shows man as having four states of consciousness:

1 The outward moving consciousness which is engrossed with the material world outside itself. This is the state of normal waking consciousness.
2 The inner moving consciousness, which is the state of dreaming.
3 The state of deep sleep.
4 The fully awakened state of Supreme Consciousness.

The first three of the four states are not to be taken literally. The state of wakeful consciousness does not mean the simple fact that one is awake, it means that consciousness whereby we are aware of the external stimuli which activate our sense perceptions. It is that consciousness of perception by which we come to know the external world.

Similarly, dream consciousness does not refer to the memory of those dreams which occur on sleep, but to the subjective consciousness which reports to the intellect, so giving rise to thoughts, emotions and desires, which are a natural reaction to the stimuli. The deep-sleep consciousness does not mean a state in which one is completely unconscious, but is that state in which object and subject blend into a unified one-ness during the process of deep concentration; it is the state in which the universal unity of all things is realised, a state which has been written of so frequently by saints, sages and poets, throughout the ages. There is universal agreement in descriptions of the first three stages of consciousness, but descriptions of the fourth tend to vary somewhat, according to the persuasion of the individual. It has been described variously as the Fourth Dimension, Transcendental Consciousness, Universal Consciousness, Supreme Bliss, and a merging into a Higher Being. It is evidently the state known in Yoga as Samadhi, and in Christianity as the Spiritual Marriage.

A more clear picture of the limitations of consciousness (or, conversely of its stages of development) may be obtained by a simple geometric analogy. Suppose, for example, we take the simple dot, made on a piece of paper with a pencil. According to definition, the dot has no dimensions, no length, breadth or depth; but if the dot were moved from its point in any direction, it would trace out a line. Now if a mind was possessed of a consciousness within the limitations of the dot, it could not imagine the concept of a line, it would be bounded by the limitations of the dot.

Similarly, if the line were moved in a direction at right angles to its length, it would trace out an area which could be represented by a four-sided figure, so giving us the concept of a plane. But a mind which was limited to the consciousness of a line only, would have no conception of a plane, and would therefore be unable to visualise or understand it.

If the plane figure were moved in a direction at right angles to itself, it would trace out the form of a solid body which we know as a cube. A mind which could live only upon a flat plane, could not conceive a cubic figure, it could not imagine a solid body.

So we come to the point that the human mind, conditioned to function in a three-dimensional world, cannot conceive that further dimension which exists beyond it.

A different analysis on consciousness is given by the Buddhist author, the Lama Anagarika Govinda in his erudite work,

Foundations of Tibetan Mysticism (published by Rider & Co.). He writes as follows:

"When in Buddhism the human personality or what we call an 'individual' has been defined as a collaboration of five groups or SKANDHAS, then this is but the description of the individual's active and reactive functions of consciousness in the sequence of their increasing density or 'materiality' and in proportion to their increasing subtlety, de-materialisation, mobility, and spiritualisation. These skandhas are:

1 Rupa-Skandha; the group of corporeality, (the sensuous), which comprises the past elements of consciousness, represented by the body; the present elements, as the sensation or idea of matter; and the future or potential sensuous elements in all their forms of appearance. This definition includes sense-organs, sense-objects, their mutual relationship and psychological consequences.

2 Vedana-Skandha: the group of feelings, which comprises all reactions derived from sense-impressions as well as from emotions arising from inner causes; i.e. feelings of pleasure and pain (bodily), joy and sorrow (mental), indifference and equanimity.

3 Samjna-Skandha: the group of perceptions of discriminating awareness and representation, which comprises the reflective or discursive as well as the intuitive faculty of discrimination.

4 Samskara-Skandha: the group of mental formations, of form-creating forces or tendencies of will, representing the active principle of consciousness, the character of the individual; namely the karmic consequences caused by conscious volition.

5 Vijnana-Skandha: the group of consciousness which comprises, combines and co-ordinates all previous functions, or represents the potentiality of consciousness in its pure, unqualified form.

The Five Skandhas correspond to the five phases which occur in every complete process of consciousness, namely:

1 Contact (of the senses with objects);

2 Feeling (identical with the definition given under vedana-skandha);

3 Perception (identical with the definition given under samjna-skandha);

4 Volition (which creates mental formations – samskara)

5 Full awareness, belonging to one of the six classes of consciousness (sight, hearing, smell, taste, body-consciousness and mind-consciousness), according to the nature of the object.''

It is evident that in the course of his evolution, man experiences several stages of consciousness, but the first stage of great importance is that at which man realises himself as an individual, the awareness of being a separate thing amongst many, one of a common species yet individually different from the rest and therefore personally unique. Turning his mind inward, he then knows himself in his true nature to be a spirit, undying and eternal, and he realises the meaning of the words "I AM".

Now that consciousness of which we have so far been speaking, is "Embodied Consciousness". In other words, through the process of evolution and the Creative Will of God, the Spirit has emerged from the Higher World to enter gradually into matter, taking the materials of earth to form about itself the physical body in which it lives. The human body has developed its particular form in order that it may become the vehicle and instrument of the Spirit, owing its shape, organs and bodily organisation, entirely to the conditioning of its environment, to enable it to live and function in earth's atmosphere and conditions.

Further proof of the adaptability of the human organism has recently been seen in the activities of the astronauts. Circling the earth outside the influence of gravitational force and air pressure, living for days under "weightless" conditions, it was found that bone structure tended to lose its properties of mechanical strength, becoming spongy and soft. It is evident from these experiments that if the human body were to be subject to such conditions for any length of time, the whole structure of the body would change, gradually but radically, to adapt itself for survival in the new conditions. Without the necessity of a strong, bony frame to support it against the pressures of earth, the human body would evolve into a shape quite unrecognisable to us as we now are, and a new creature would be created. The mind and the soul would still be there, but the physical vehicle would necessarily be different in shape and dimension.

Science fiction has made use of such facts to paint lurid pictures of different forms of life existing upon other planets, usually having a high degree of intelligence, and being antagonistic to man. If one seriously considers the evidence we now have, and the fact that man, in his true nature, is a spirit, it then appears eminently feasible to assume that life does exist on other planets, though in different forms. This theory is corroborated by clairvoyants throughout the world.

This simply means that the Universal Spirit has moved in another area of the universe, using the materials of that particular area to form a vehicle for itself in sympathy with its environment, through which it may manifest and operate.

Science has proved that the basic substances of the universe are the same on all planets, differences being only in degree, according to a particular planet. Man, in himself, being formless and un-substantial, it is not difficult to accept that Spirit, acting upon matter as described in our earlier chapter, can take upon itself any form it chooses, and in any place it chooses, according to the desires and dictates of the Divine Creative Will.

So far we have been speaking of that consciousness which is immanent in mind and matter which is known as "Embodied Consciousness". That Consciousness to which the Yogi aspires, however, is its first and greatest aspect, which is "Transcendental Consciousness". This has been called the "Supreme Consciousness", the Universal Consciousness", the "Pure Consciousness", which, through its own power, creates mind and matter. This is the Consciousness of Spirit, which is ever an indivisible unity. Mind and Matter are manifestations of Spirit which appear in many different forms and degrees. The latter can be seen by simply looking at the world about us, the various peoples of the world and the folk we meet in our everyday life. All have differing degrees of awareness, and most have their consciousness rooted in the material things of the world, seeing no further. Life can be seen similarly in many forms, but as we have already seen, the basic building blocks of all things, whether living or inanimate, are the ubiquitous atoms. The atom itself is composed of even smaller particles, whose almost infinite variety of combination creates the many different substances and forms which go to make up our world.

It is this common basis of all things which gives rise to the concept of Maya, or illusion, for all things are in fact a common unity, all things are one in their essence. The Eastern philosophy in relating all things to their origin in the subtle world, sees the manifold forms and substances of the world as an illusion which is created by the limitations of our own human senses of perception. This philosophy shows how the Supreme Consciousness has veiled itself in earthly matter of differing degrees of density and diversity of form in the process of involution. It is shown as the task of evolution to break through the illusion to the True Reality which lies veiled behind it. It is the process of Yoga to teach man how this may be achieved in the space of one brief lifetime.

We can now perceive consciousness as a dichotomy, one part of which is immanent in man, the second part being transcendent to him. Both forms of consciousness are one in the same sense in which the spectrum of light is really one in essence, and it is clearly only a matter of knowledge and application which will enable man to lift his consciousness from the Immanent to the Transcendent. This is the teaching of Raja Yoga.

One of the most powerful aids in the process of mental elevation is Prayer. The Catholic Catechism defines prayer as "the raising of the heart and mind to God", and no clearer definition could be found, for in these few words lies a complete guide along the Path to God. The nature of Prayer is only too often misunderstood. The dictionary defines it as "to ask earnestly, or to earnestly entreat". In this, prayer is seen only as a process of asking for something, or entreating God's help. Not that this is wrong, for it is the most natural thing in the world that a child should ask its father for help in time of trouble, or for some particular favour. But this is only the smallest, the most elementary part of Prayer, and is rooted in materialism. It is, however, the first stage in the process of orientating the mind to God, a process which should culminate in Spiritual Union. When Jesus said, "Ask and ye shall receive", He was not referring to material benefits.

It is right and proper that we should see God as a Father figure, for is He not the Father of the whole universe? But if we are to achieve spiritual elevation, we must progress beyond this kind of imagery, which sees God as an exalted super-human.

Dr. Alexis Carrel, winner of the Nobel Prize in 1912, said, "Certain spiritual activities may cause anatomical as well as functional modification of tissues and organs. These organic phenomena are observed in various circumstances, among them being the state of prayer.

"Prayer should be understood, not as a mere mechanical reiteration of formulae but as a mystical elevation, an absorption of consciousness in the contemplation of a principle both permeating and transcending our world."

Helen Rhodes Wallace in *How to Enter The Silence*, writes, "Effectual prayer is a process of releasing by means of the human instrument, certain elements necessary to bring about the answer. . . . Devotion is a degree of mental pressure that enables consciousness to move out of the conflict of cross purposes, into a centre of calm."

Jesus taught that ". . . you will receive abundantly . . . according to the Power that worketh in you." Is this not the power of the working of Prayer?

St. James put this another way when he said, "The supplication of a righteous man availeth much in its working" (Chapter 1/5–6).

By force of habit, created by early training, it is customary for most Christians to repeat those prayers which they learnt as children, or to read from a prayer book. Whilst this practice has much to commend it in the elementary stages of spiritual growth, as an aid to meditation, it happens only too often that by continual repetition over the years, the words begin to lose their meaning and fail to hold the attention. The mind then begins to wander aimlessly as a state of near-coma is approached, the parrot-like vocalisation having a hypnotic effect which does nothing to assist spiritual elevation.

Prayer is of no use unless it is charged with the forces of love and spiritual desire. A strong and sustained effort is needed to control the mind in the first place, to hold it to its point in "raising the heart and mind to God". Prayer is a vital instrument in our work of spiritual advancement, and has been proved by saints and seers through the years to be the surest vehicle by which one may ascend to God.

To return to our definition, we can perceive two distinct paths by which the Supreme may be approached. The first part of our definition focuses attention upon the heart, and as we have seen in our earlier work, the heart is the seat of Divine Love. By thus meditating, we direct our attention, and so our consciousness, along the Path of Devotion which is taught in Bhakta Yoga. The power generated by an intense love and desire for the Divine will carry us far along the Path of Attainment.

Every act of devotion is an act of "raising the heart to God". Whether the act is involved in religious ceremonial, reciting a prayer, or an act of devotion or charity to a fellow-man, if properly directed it becomes a spiritual offering. Even a humble task performed in the pursuit of our daily life, if offered in a spirit of devotion becomes, in itself, a prayer, serving to open the heart to God and the influence of the Holy Spirit, from whence the healing graces may flow inwards in a life-giving stream.

The second part of our definition was to "raise the mind", and this most important aspect of prayer we shall deal with when we come to discuss Meditation, later in this chapter.

One of the most complete prayers was given us by Jesus in the "Lord's Prayer". This covers almost every phase of our needs, both physical and spiritual. Even the first two words, "Our Father", constitute a prayer, for in this brief phrase there lies a world of love, hope and trust. In them we acknowledge God as the Supreme Being, our Creator and Spiritual Father, and we call His attention to us, His children. Meditating upon these two words alone, one feels a strong sense of an all-encompassing protection, an all-embracing Divine Love which dissolves all fear and anxiety.

"Who art in Heaven", the next phrase, leads us to thought of a Higher World and to the realisation of Christ's teaching that "The Kingdom of Heaven lies within us". As the all-pervading Supreme Being, God is immanent in all things, dwelling both within and without us. We may look at His wonders which abound in the world external to us in awe and humility, and in these we can see the very presence of God. But in truth He is even nearer, for He dwells in that inner kingdom of the Self, whose realisation is our true goal. The Isa Upanishad tells us, "He is far and He is near. He is within all and He is outside all." The Katha Upanishad (Parts 1 and 3), says, "The light of the Atman (spirit) is invisible, concealed in all beings. It is seen by seers of the subtle, with clear and inner vision." Again, in Part 2, Chapter 1, the Katha Upanishad says, "The soul dwells within us, a flame the size of a thumb. When this is known as the Lord, then ceases all fear." Where Divine Love exists, there can be no fear.

In the next phrase, the Holy Name is venerated. "Hallowed be Thy Name." This is a phase of worship which appears to be more cultivated in the east than the west. A Hindu telling his beads, is practising Japa Mala, repeating over and over again the names of God, believing that the vibrations released in this way will assist him in his efforts to raise his consciousness above the limitations of self, and by their very nature will attract to him those Graces of the Spirit which he is seeking.

"Thy Kingdom Come, Thy Will be done", is an act of submission in which we surrender ourselves to the Will of God. Without such complete surrender of the personal ego, there can be no inflow of Divine Grace. The personal ego is the greatest barrier to spiritual advancement. Its desires and vain opinions form opposing forces which the Spirit does not penetrate (except in such cases as St. Paul, where the spiritual forces necessary to overcome his powerful antagonism were so great as to leave him paralysed and blind). Voluntary submission to the Divine Will, and suppression of the ego are essential if we are to experience the joys and the gifts of the Spirit. Otherwise, we cannot even begin to know God.

Up to this point our hearts will have been directed to expression of love and veneration for our Creator. From this point on, we then ask our Father for those blessings and graces which will enable us to live in peace and harmony. "Give us this day our daily bread", is a supplication for sustenance both spiritual and physical. "Man does not live by bread alone", said Jesus, and so we ask our Father to give to us the blessing of His inflowing Grace, the true food of the Spirit, so that we may have the strength and the wisdom to withstand and surmount the problems and stresses which are an inevitable part of our daily life.

We have said that God is immanent in all things. If we admit also His knowledge of all things, this must include knowledge of our daily needs, so that one may be tempted to ask why it is necessary for one to pray for something of which the Almighty Father, omniscient and all-knowing, is already aware. One may also point to Jesus' admonition, "Our Father knoweth what is needful for you before you ask him". (Matthew VI/8.) Again

Jesus says, "Be not solicitous therefore, saying: What shall we eat, or what shall we drink, or wherewith shall we be clothed? For after all these things do the heathens seek. For your Father knoweth that you have need of all these things. Seek ye therefore first the Kingdom of God, and His Justice, and all these things shall be added unto you" (Matthew VI/31–32). This is a clear confirmation from the highest authority that our Father is indeed aware of all our needs, and so we may ask again, "Why pray for something of which God is already aware?"

The answer is that it is essential that the heart and mind be opened to God's Grace by prayer, for if we simply leave everything to God in the assumption that He will automatically provide for us with no effort on our parts, we only succeed in closing those channels through which the life-giving forces may pass to us. Prayer is both the vehicle and the channel, for in raising our minds to God we attune ourselves to spiritual influences which bring to us inspiration, wisdom and strength.

Gradually, through perseverance and a sincere desire to serve God, the consciousness begins to expand with the inflow of Grace. By degrees, a spiritual awakening takes place, until during meditation inner perception becomes sufficiently powerful for Spiritual Union to take place. Without the development of this inner perception there can be little progress, and if this does not improve we must look into our own hearts for the cause. It may then be seen that the mind is taken up by worldly desires and delusions of the ego, which, if allowed to continue, will make of prayer no more than a vain repetition of empty words which will have no meaning. Without the force of an urgent desire for the Spirit, there can be no penetration of the "Cloud of Unkowing", which veils us from our true Self.

To be effective, prayer must have Power, Sincerity and Meaning.

The example which immediately springs to mind is that of the Centurion (Matthew VIII/8), who, on telling Jesus of his servant, lying at home grievously ill, was told by Jesus, "I will come and heal him". The Centurion then spoke those words which were to become immortalised, which are still repeated by Christians the world over, "Lord, I am not worthy that thou shouldst enter under my roof, say but the Word and my servant shall be healed." The power of appeal and its sincerity were duly rewarded, "And the servant was healed at that same hour" (Matthew VIII/13).

The Mundaka Upanishad says (Part 2, Chapter 2, 3–4): "Take up the great bow of the Upanishad (sacred scripture) and place in it an arrow made sharp with devotion. Draw the bow with concentration upon God and hit the centre of the mark, the same Everlasting Spirit. The bow is the sacred word OM (see *Yoga The Key to Life*, pages 138–9), and the arrow is the Self. God is the mark of the arrow and the aim of the soul. Even as the arrow stays resting in its mark, let the vigilant Self rest in its aim."

In the book entitled, *The Cloud of Unknowing*, the work of an anonymous and ancient mystic, the "Cloud" is given as that which veils man's consciousness from his Spirit, creating in man the ignorance of "unknowing". The author writes that we are to visualise ourselves hurling the name of Jesus at the Cloud like the aiming of the arrow in the Upanishad. We are told to visualise the arrow as penetrating the Cloud to emerge in the splendour of the Spirit beyond. Such visualisation, if powered by strong desire and determination, is yet another way of opening the mind to God. We know that thought is a dynamic force. If it is properly directed it will surely pierce the "Cloud of Unknowing", and open up for us the Path to the Spirit.

When, in the Lord's Prayer, we beseech Him to "Forgive us our trespasses", we also commit ourselves to forgive in like manner, "as we forgive those who trespass against us". In this we remind ourselves that we cannot expect from our Father, something which we are not prepared ourselves to give. But this is no simple matter, for to say simply, "I forgive", has no meaning unless it is accompanied by the emotion of complete forgiveness from the heart. When a wrong is done to us, it is natural to feel resentment and anger, even to harbour thoughts of revenge, of "having our own back".

We must learn to recognise these emotions and mental attitudes as no more than legacies left over from the days of the beast, when perhaps man's survival depended upon his will to fight, to retaliate, to become aggressive. Knowing that such emotions are no longer necessary, but can only react to our own disadvantage, we must, when they occur, bring them out into the open and regard them as dispassionately as possible. Looking at their cause and effect, we can only agree that they are useless, unworthy, and more than likely damaging and disturbing to ourselves rather than to the person giving rise to them. Anger is particularly malignant, for it pours chemicals into the system which poison, over-stressing nerves and tissue whilst raising blood pressure to dangerous limits. If such anger is persisted in and allowed to become habitual, it is inevitable that the health will suffer in one way or another, there can be no peace of mind, and joy must be a permanent stranger. Anger, seen clairvoyantly in the human aura, is a terrible thing. The aura becomes darkened like a stormy cloud, and flaming tongues of colour dart through it in vicious streaks of red.

Forgiveness implies, not simply the verbal expression which pays only lip service to virtue, but complete eradication of any antagonistic emotion resultant upon the particular transgression, replacing this with feelings of love and charity. We know from our earlier work (*Yoga The Key to Life*) that any thought, word or action, leaves its impression upon the subtle akasa, permanent, indelible, and reflecting upon future thought and action. Forgiveness, in its real sense, means the complete eradication of such impressions (Sanskaras), but as this also involves the cancellation of the Karmic effects, such complete eradication is within the power of God alone. On the human plane, we can come nearest to such perfect forgiveness by emanating feelings of love and charity. This is the real meaning of the admonition to "turn the other cheek", and in so doing we go far in our own spiritual advancement, thereby growing in strength and understanding, becoming more "in tune" with the Spirit of God.

It has been said that "to know all is to forgive all", and in this one is taught to strive to see the reason or the cause of the transgression we have suffered. In every act one can see the effect of some previous cause, though the latter is generally hidden from us. It frequently happens that if only we could be made aware of the primary cause of actions by others which displease or hurt us, we would feel only pity for those concerned, a pity which would drive out anger, to leave only compassion in its place.

The final plea in the Lord's Prayer, is that He "Lead us not into temptation, but deliver us from evil". This is by no means a plea to be "let off" from all temptation, for if this did occur we would never be able to develop character and spiritual strength, so that we could never develop will power. Without will and character degeneration could be the only result.

In this magnificent and all-embracing Lord's Prayer, one can perceive a clear guide to the manner of prayer in general. Our earlier definition of prayer shows it as a process which involves the whole man. In "raising the heart" the emotions are involved in an act which directs them in a spirit of love and veneration to our Father. This is the Way of Devotion, and is the Way of Bhakta Yoga. In "raising the mind to God", we direct every part of our mental make-up to that Sphere which lies beyond the physical. In so doing, we learn control of thought and so of mind, and control of our senses. Our whole being is then aimed like the arrow of the Upanishad to God, so that in finding its mark we may come to greater love and knowledge of God. This is the Way of Intellect or the Way of Mind, which is also the Way of Raja Yoga. Bhakta Yoga and Raja Yoga in their elementary stages are already practised by every Christian. The main difference lies in the fact that, whereas the student of Yoga knows exactly what he is doing, why he is doing it, and the effects he wishes to achieve, the Christian is left to rely largely upon his elementary theological teaching gained at school, and to the degree of faith he is able to bring to it. A fuller knowledge as given by Yoga, together with the practical techniques of Yoga which lead to self-improvement, are of considerable aid in bringing the teachings by which one may attain a life which is completely satisfying. Many dark corners are illuminated by the philosophies of Yoga, and with this fuller knowledge comes confidence, peace of mind, health and joy.

One aspect of prayer which has hitherto been neglected, but which appears to be coming to the fore, is its application to healing. Whether this be called "Faith healing", "Spirit healing", "Psychic healing", "Magnetic healing", or "Pranic healing", the basic mechanism is the same. It is only the method of approach which differs. Jesus "gave to His apostles the power to heal all manner of diseases and all manner of infirmities . . . commanding them to heal the sick, raise the dead, cleanse the lepers. . . . For it is not you that speak, but the Spirit of your Father who speaketh in you" (Matthew Chapter X/2–22). The message is thus clear enough, but the Christian Churches, although they have carried out most faithfully Jesus' command to "teach all nations", appear to have for the most part neglected this vital part of their Ministry, to heal the sick.

However, our purpose is to study the subject of Prayer, and we must not digress into argument on healing, fascinating though it is.

Apart from the power which we know is inherent in word and thought, whose vibratory effects have already been discussed, in the act of praying for healing we also make of ourselves a channel through which the healing graces may flow. Healing was an important part of Jesus' ministry, for, apart from its practical demonstration of his own personal powers, it gave visible evidence of the existence of a world beyond the physical, a world of powerful forces which, with man as an intermediary and instrument, is capable of performing super-normal acts of healing which we call "miracles". The entire universe is governed by Law, and from the mass of evidence which has now accumulated it is clear that there is a Law which involves healing, and to those who are spiritually gifted is given the power to operate this Law, either consciously or otherwise. Prayer, "the raising of the heart and mind to God", is an essential part of the healing process.

Prayer leads naturally into Meditation. A meditation is usually begun with a prayer to assist in clearing the mind of extraneous thought, to orientate it towards the Spirit, and to concentrate the mental energies. From the state of prayer one moves into a state of meditation.

Meditation, however, is a practice which proves a stumbling-block to almost all beginners. Many would-be mystics fall by the wayside at this juncture, failing in the patience and perseverance which are essential for success. It is not possible to jump straight into meditation with hopes of immediate reward, for much depends upon the stage of development and the state of mind of the individual, and in any case, much preliminary work is necessary in training the will and control of mind.

In the excited eagerness which follows each new discovery, there lies a tendency for the beginner to haunt the libraries and bookstalls reading book after book in quick succession as the enthusiasm takes hold. All this is laudable in many respects, but it can only lead to confusion if persisted in, as well as dissipating uselessly those energies which should be applied circumspectly along a definite path of instruction.

In a deep study such as this, one must guard against the

modern technique of "fast scanning", which, although a valuable time-saving device in business where so much paper-work has to be got through in time which is never adequate, it has the inherent disadvantage of giving only a fleeting impression. It is an impression which can leave no lasting mark, so that the information can only be held in the mind for a short time, being soon pushed out by the next piece of information. Only a full effort of concentration can suffice in a subject which involves complete re-orientation of mind and deep thinking on the part of the student. Therefore it is advisable that when reading the subject, one should read no more than a paragraph at a time, or just so much as is necessary to convey the author's meaning; then, closing the eyes and the book, make a critical analysis of what has just been read, ensure that its full meaning has been grasped, and then put this into perspective with what has been learnt to date. This may take time, but its value far outweighs the effort.

The next point to be realised is that personal application is essential to progress. The real teacher is experience and not mere intellectual knowledge. An awareness of facts as related by others who have undergone experience, may bring belief, but to obtain true knowledge one must also undergo that same experience. Practice is therefore the keynote of success – Jesus taught that "Faith without works is dead".

The situation of the beginner is also made more difficult by the fact that he is unable to obtain immediate proof of what he reads, and must therefore go forward in faith alone, until prayer and practice provide the proof he needs. Understanding grows with deepening knowledge but understanding is a condition into which one evolves, it cannot be achieved quickly or without sacrifice and effort.

Where, then, does the practice of Meditation fit into the general scheme of things?

Meditation can be described as a practice whereby mind and soul are orientated to the things of Spirit by shutting out all physical sense perceptions, and by putting down all thoughts not relevant to the subject of the meditation. Man thereby opens his own personal channel to the Spirit, bringing into life his own Spiritual Centre, through which he is able to communicate consciously with the Higher Worlds. The limited personal mind in this condition is transcended, as normal consciousness expands into Super-consciousness. In "The Silence", the soul then knows its True Self and finds True Knowledge.

This is the sphere of "the Power and the Glory", and in common with all other of God's creations, responds to certain, definite, laws. These laws operate on the common basis of cause and effect with which we are familiar, the cause being the dynamic force necessary to create the desired effect. The force in this case is the force of mind, operating dynamically in the subtle sphere to create the modifications whose images we hold in mind, and which must be so held, clear and strong.

In meditation, there are three conditions of which one must beware. The first of these is the habit of lethargy, when meditation becomes no more than a comfortable day-dream. From the point of spiritual advancement this is quite useless, and, indeed, can lead to mental deterioration. The second condition is that mind-wandering which follows upon association of ideas, when a word unconsciously generates a following train of thought which leads away from the subject, one thing following upon another, until we suddenly awake to the fact that we are thinking about something entirely different from our starting point. The third condition is one which sometimes has a rather startling effect upon the unprepared beginner, who suddenly finds thoughts arising within him which, if not positively evil, have a strong tendency in that direction.

Do not be discouraged by this latter phase, for it is a natural phenomenon. In all of us there are still traces of those animal instincts by which man has survived his fight through the evolutionary jungle. Also, in the subconscious mind there exists a whole dustbin-full of repressed urges and thoughts which have their origin in our animal self. When the mind has been stilled and all thought supressed, there appears a mental vacuum. But nature abhors a vacuum in any form and will always try to fill it, so that the subconscious mind takes this opportunity to throw upon the screen of the conscious mind, all those things which civilisation and religion have taught us to repress. In order to clear this situation and to purge such things from the subconscious, it is only necessary to drag these thoughts and urges into the light of full consciousness, to analyse and rationalise them, so that they may then be consciously discarded by an effort of will, a command to the mind, regarding them for the useless and harmful things they really are.

In this way we also learn to demonstrate the power of will, which is strengthened thereby, this practice also assisting in the process of purification. According to those laws which we have referred to, it is not possible for spiritual life to be approached with any success until the mind has been properly prepared, purified and orientated. Spiritual development will be inhibited as long as we allow ourselves to remain indolent and weak-willed.

Fear of the unknown is often a barrier to progress, but this is overcome when ignorance gives way to knowledge. To know is to cast out fear. The stress and strain of personal contacts in a competitive world leave their turmoil in the mind, but also tend to rouse in us the tiger of anger which must be tamed by the practice of personal detachment, the serpent of envy which must be destroyed by rational thought, and the demon of greed who must be overcome by self-sacrifice. The daily practice of meditation will create a mental haven in which the peace and joy of the Spirit will replace the worldly stress and strife.

In this respect it is interesting to note that experiments being carried out currently in America, have shown that the metabolic rate of the body, and hence the "rate of working" of the body, are changed during the three stages of consciousness, namely, the normal state of waking consciousness, the state of sleep in which one dreams, and the state of deep, dreamless, sleep. In the latter state it has been found that a healing process takes places which is extremely beneficial, particularly in cases of mental stress and nervous disorder. Experiment has proved that the same metabolic condition, and the same healing process, take place in a state of meditation.

However, to resume our discussion on those obstacles which we must learn to overcome on our Path of Attainment, it is relevant to note what the Eastern philosophies have to say. Swami Sivananda, for example, said in a lecture given at Lakhimpur in 1932, "There are certain obstacles in the path of Yoga which you should by all means overcome in the beginning of your Yogic career. If you do not adequately guard yourself against these impediments in right time, they will smash all your hopes and aspirations to pieces and will eventually bring about miserable downfall.

"Lust, greed, anger, jealousy, fear, inertia, depression, prejudice, intolerance, evil company, arrogance, self-sufficiency, desire for name and fame, building castles in the air, curiosity and hypocrisy, are the foremost amongst these. You should ever introspect and watch your mind; you should take effective measures to remove these obstacles root and branch."

Sivananda then goes on to teach just how these obstacles may be overcome.

The Siva Samhita says of meditation, "It is the Seventh Limb of Yoga, and in the Sanskrit is called 'Dhyana'. Its purpose is to lead man to a spiritual experience in which he enters into a personal and conscious relationship with God."

Helen Rhodes Wallace writes, "To enter the Silence (in meditation), means to turn the mind inward, focusing the mind upon a God-word, meditating upon it and in it until it flashes into reality, and the mental field is alive with it."

Professor William James said, "Under certain conditions, there is an influx of a higher order of consciousness, when something from above takes hold of a lower part of itself, quickening it with a new morality, often utterly re-creating the outer man." (In this respect one is reminded of the conversion of St. Paul, although this was a more forceful and drastic event than the gentle process of meditation.)

Brother Lawrence in *The Practice of The Presence of God*, describes his experience as follows: "Somehow I found myself changed all at once, and my soul, which till that time was in trouble, felt a profound and inward peace, as if it had found a place of rest."

Meditation flows smoothly and without conscious effort into contemplation, when the Self becomes absorbed in the Spirit. In Yoga this is the state of Samadhi, which Swami Sivanada describes as, ". . . the fruit of meditation. Samadhi is a super-conscious state wherein the Yogin gets super-intuitional, super-sensual knowledge and super-sensual bliss. He gets the vision of the Lord. He is in a state of communion with the Lord. He is in full enjoyment of the Divine Ecstasy. He has now seen the Light of Lights."

Meditation, then, is a continuous flow of thought, concentrated upon a particular subject in an ordered form and without deviation. In pursuance of our own particular subject, the enquiry is to be directed within ourselves in order that we may come to know our true Self, and so assist the expansion of our consciousness into the Higher World where dwells the "Light of Lights".

Meditation is clearly essential in pursuance of the Path of Attainment. It must therefore be understood and practised with all the patience and perseverance, enthusiasm and devotion, of which we are capable. It is a most important link in the chain of Samyama (concentration, meditation and contemplation), but the preceding links must be thoroughly forged or only disappointment will be the result.

In the early stages meditation is fatiguing, both physically and mentally, but Yoga offers the techniques by which both may be overcome. Postures which are conducive to meditation must be held for some time, and although the Lotus posture, in which the Yogi is seated cross-legged for many hours at a time, has become the classical pattern, this is difficult for the western student to achieve. There are, however, a number of postures from which one may choose, the principle being that the frame must remain upright in a locked position, so that the body will not fall over from fatigue or simple imbalance, and the spine must be in stright line with the head, so that the subtle forces may flow without hindrance. Proper breathing is essential to concentration, and this also is assisted by choosing the right posture. These techniques are given in the study of Hatha Yoga. (See *Yoga The Key to Life*.)

Having established our chosen posture, the next step in approaching meditation is to establish physical and mental harmony by relaxation and rhythmic breathing. The psycho-somatic effects of the latter will create a perfect state of physical and mental calm in which thought is readily controlled and will flow more easily into the stream of meditation.

Concentration is the next step, in which all mental efforts are directed to blocking unwanted and irrelevant thought from the mind. In this exercise, the principal difficulty is to contain the thoughts within the subject of our meditation and not allow them to wander off in another direction. The prime cause of such mind-wandering as we have said, is the association of ideas, which automatically, though imperceptibly, lead thought away from its subject, when we suddenly awaken to the fact that our mind is engaged with something which is far distant, irrelevant to the subject of our meditation. It is essential also that our thought be clearly defined, in order to create a concise image in the mind. Half formulated ideas and vague imagery will lead only to torpor, lacking the force and the clear direction in which creation can take place.

To train the mind in concentration and clear imagery, it is both wise and helpful to begin by practising with simple and familiar objects. Let us take for an example a simple jug. The jug is placed before us, and we take up our chosen posture, perfectly relaxed and with rhythmic breathing established. We then fix our gaze, steady and unswerving, upon the jug. Concentration is greatly assisted in the early stages by repeating orally the name of the object of concentration. So in this case we repeat the word, "jug", pausing slightly between each utterance, thus creating a rhythm of speech – pause – speech – pause. In this first phase it is only necessary to impress upon the mind, the image of the jug, so that we see "jug", we speak "jug", we feel "jug", and our whole field of consciousness becomes "jug". The mind will inevitably tend to wander sometimes to some idea or thing associated with "jug", but must be brought back again to the subject until it can be held unwaveringly upon "jug" and nothing else. It is also helpful to take note of the number of times the mind is found to wander, first in a minute, then in two minutes and so on, until the time has been extended for some minutes in which concentration has been held.

We may next continue with concentrated gaze, but omit the spoken word, holding the mind to the jug. The eyes should be kept open until they begin to water, when concentration may be broken off and the eyes rested. The eyes are then closed, and an effort made to hold the image of the jug in the mind as long as possible without fading.

When this has been accomplished and the image held in the mind without deviation for some time, a deeper meditation on the jug may then be attempted. Now, every detail must be assimilated, the shape, the colour, the texture, the substance, until we almost feel a part of the jug itself. The process is similar to the exercise given on pages 27–28 of *Yoga The Key to Life*.

Having absorbed every possible bit of information in this way, the eyes are again closed and an attempt made to recall every detail we have just learnt, letting these flow through the mind in an unbroken stream of thought. In this way, concentration is developed and the mind trained in the process of meditation, which is the state of "unbroken flow of thought".

We may now pass on to study meditation in its deeper sense. Its purpose and principle can best be established by a study of the Mandala. These are designs composed of geometric forms, symbols and images, by which the mind is led in pre-determined steps to become finally absorbed, deeply, in the spiritual subject which is the object of the meditation and the purpose of the Mandala. The Lama Anagarika Govinda describes the Mandala as, "a systematic arrangement of symbols on which the process of visualisation is based. It is generally based upon a 4-, 8-, 16-petalled lotus blossom, which forms the starting point of the meditation."

Starting at a particular point or symbol on the Mandala, the mind is led deeper and deeper into the subject, being gradually induced to build up the desired image and all its attributes, upon which the meditation then proceeds. As meditation deepens, mind becomes more and more involved with object, until finally a fusion takes place in which both are one and meditation flows into contemplation. Environment and atmosphere are all-important, and it assists if music is played softly in the background, whilst some find it relaxing and helpful to burn incense. These, however, are a matter for personal experiment and choice.

The Catholic, meditating upon the Rosary, holds in mind those things with which he desires to attain spiritual affinity. The Holy Family, Mary, the Mother of Jesus, the Way of the Cross, perhaps most of all the Person of Christ Himself; these are typical subjects of Catholic meditation. The statues and murals seen in Christian churches are intended to assist meditation in this way, providing a focal point for concentration and helping to build up imagery in the mind. If the exercises given in the preceding are carried out sincerely, it should then be possible for one's desired image to be projected in the mind at any time, so that in time of stress, or when it is proposed to meditate, the physical emblems eventually become unnecessary, for the mind has now absorbed all the essentials of its subject, which can be recalled at will.

Meditation is an essential ingredient of all religions, it is also the keystone of Yoga. It is the primary teaching of Raja Yoga but is practised principally in Jnana Yoga and Laya Yoga in connection with the Chakras, or psychic centres. In Jnana Yoga one meditates upon the inner Self, and comes to know this by the process of introspective self-analysis. This is dealt with more fully in Chapter XI of *Yoga The Key to Life*, to which the reader is recommended to refer, and in which the subject "Who am I", is discussed, and the techniques which lead the mind deeper into man's inner life, where his true Self abides, and where union with the Divine Spirit may be achieved.

The practice of such meditations renders the sense perceptions ever more acute, so that one becomes more and more influenced by the vibrations of the Higher Worlds. Inevitably, one becomes more responsive to finer influences and emotions as character, personality, and even the physical body, become more refined through refinement of mind and the working of the Spirit. Mental tranquillity and bodily harmony will follow as sure as night follows day, for both must operate within and in accordance with the Law.

Our world is at present undergoing a painful transition to a new order of living. What this will be, is difficult to see in the midst of the current violence and anarchy. But one thing must be destroyed in order to make place for the new and better, and such change is ever painful, full of doubts and difficulties and strife, with man set against man in forceful antagonism. In these circumstances one must hold fast to Faith with strength and the courage of one's convictions, for the forces of God (Good) must prevail, and the evolutionary process inevitably destroys that which is weak and unable to sustain itself. The daily practice of meditation will prove a healing balm in such a situation. Ragged nerves will be soothed and tensions drained away, whilst doubts and fears disappear before the soft, reassuring voice of the Spirit. Is it not foolish to deny ourselves this wonderful gift of the Spirit. It is ours for the sake of only a few minutes each day, spent alone and in silence, where the Voice may be heard.

CHAPTER 10

Sadhaka, Sadhana and Dharma

Once it has been accepted that the true basis of Man's personality is spiritual, that he is essentially a spiritual being incarnated upon earth for a particular purpose, it is inevitable that the urge for further knowledge arises. An expanding consciousness develops, bringing with it an awareness which encompasses a wider range of apprehension and a growing sensitivity to the promptings of inner forces, and reactions to external stimuli.

The finer points of life begin to make themselves apparent. Appreciation of beauty, a growing sense of compassion, a general feeling of expansion, are all signs of the awakening spirit. It is unfortunately true that such stirrings of the spirit can also operate in the opposite direction, there being polarity in all things. This gives rise to egotism, greed for power and possessions, vain pride, violent nationalism, and in the extreme, attraction to drugs, debauchery and witchcraft.

In the light of this knowledge, it becomes even more urgent that man is made aware of his spiritual origin, that spiritual forces are at work both within him and without, that man has free will to develop these for his own expansion and evolution to a finer being, according to the Laws of Karma, or he may use them to satisfy baser instincts which lead only to violence, destruction and spiritual death.

The Spiritual Path is not an easy one to tread, for it involves a belief in that which cannot be proved, a denial of many things which give pleasure, a strict control over the "animal" man, and complete devotion to a God who remains unheard and unseen.

The first blossoming on the Path is the awakening of the Inner Self, the first awareness that man is more than the sum of his parts, a deep feeling of the urge to KNOW and to expand.

The teachings of Vedanta and the Upanishads have opened the eyes of many in both east and west, to the profound truths which lie behind Man's existence, and have opened the door leading to the Path of Attainment.*

The aspirant on the Path, the seeker after spiritual knowledge, is known in Yoga as the "Sadhaka". The spiritual disciplines to which he subjects himself, his endeavours to lead a "spiritual" life, indeed, the very life he leads as an aspirant upon the Path, is Sadhana.†

How, then, does this affect the ordinary individual, the "man in the streeet", who has no aspiration for saintly asceticism, but who simply wishes to be assured of eternal spiritual life, to live life in his own way, and to be satisfied at the end that he has done all things it has been in his power to do.

Well, we have already seen that the Path of Desire is for the beginner, he whose eyes are beginning to open to the Truth and to what is Real. In this, although it is conceded that desires are a natural part of man's make-up and must occur in all people at all times, it is taught that all desires must be subject to scrutiny and evaluation to ensure that they are rightly motivated, that they are orientated to what is permanent, enduring and of lasting joy instead of to what is transitory, unsatisfying and leading in the end to damnation.

Briefly, the answer is "Study and Action". In the first place one has much to learn, from books, from lectures, from people, from experience, and by no means least, from the inner voice.

Even the most brilliant scientist, engineer, artist or mathematician must first learn the basic language of their craft, the history of its development, and an assessment of where it now stands. He must then decide where he stands personally with what has gone before and what is now being taught.

So the Sadhaka is referred to the Scriptures, the sacred writings hallowed by time and confirmed by the experiences of many generations. We are told that history repeats itself, but if the lessons of the past are properly learnt and applied, then, surely, only that which is good will be repeated. It is a tragic fact

---

* See *The Sword of Destiny* by Arthur Trevor Ravenscroft, published by Neville Spearman & Co. Documentary evidence is presented that Hitler, having studied Yoga and Vedanta, was attracted to the "Left-hand Path", became possessed, practising witchcraft and Blak Magic.

† For a typical schedule see *Yoga The Key to Life* (frontispiece).

that man continues to make the same fundamental mistakes today that his ancestors have made throughout man's history, and so he continues to reap the sorrows which inevitably result.

So often history records the rise of men, often from the lower strata of society, men whose brilliance and dedication have won them places as leaders of men, only to find that a lust for power, greed, egotism or sensuality has diverted them from their initial high purpose, to create mass suffering, hatred and final disaster, where there should have been peace, plenty and joy.

Study of the Scriptures, and all the learning of the world, are sterile, unless they are accompanied by that action which puts them into practice. Knowledge of itself is no more than an intellectual exercise, and we are warned in all the Scriptures of the dangers of literal knowledge, without appreciating also the spiritual values behind them, and, of still greater importance, of putting them into practice.

"How can books enlighten that lump of clay which is man, if man does not learn the Truth when it is explained to him" (from Naishkarmyasiddhi).

"Fools dwelling in ignorance, wise in their own conceit and vain knowledge are like the blind leading the blind" (Katha-Upanishad).

The great seers of the past have become the great Teachers, and around their teachings religions have sprung up as more disciples and adherents are gathered under the Teacher's Banner.

All religions therefore provide a path which will lead to Self-Realisation, in which man Realises the Divinity within himself. The fact that some religions are now so overlaid with materialism that much of the esoteric meaning has been lost, and with it the true teaching, is not our concern in this book. Suffice to say that in all religions the Truth is there. "Seek and ye shall find" was the teaching of Jesus.

Once a man has accepted a particular religion to be the most suitable for his spiritual progress, he is thereby committed to follow its precepts, to carry out the requirements laid down by the Fathers of the Church.

In some eastern religions, the practice of their faith appears to be carried much more into their everyday lives than is so in the West, where "Church-on-Sunday" often seems to approach a mere social occasion, the rest of the week being devoted to profit and pleasure.

I once heard an old priest admonish his flock one Sunday, when he told them, "The trouble with most of you is that on Sundays you pray on your knees, whilst the rest of the week you prey on each other," a comment frequently not far from the truth!

However, the living of life in accordance with the circumstances into which one was born is man's Dharma. All religions call upon us to fulfil our duties to the best of our abilities, both at home and at work, spiritually and materially, always with a spirit of self-sacrifice and devotion.

Life has a purpose and a part of that purpose is that each one of us is introduced into those circumstances which will best suit his or her spiritual advancement. The family into which we are born, the work or profession in which we become engaged, the many events and situations which arise during our lifetime, all serve as problems to be overcome, exercises in the game of Life, in which we gain strength, character, understanding and a further step along the Path to Perfection.

This then is man's Dharma, sometimes simply referred to as "duty" sometimes as "the essential nature of a thing".

Combining the two definitions we get that man's "essential nature" is spiritual and that it is his "duty" to manifest this True Self.

During the Vedic Period in India, and for many years thereafter, the community was divided into four social groups, in what is now known as the "Caste System". The Brahmanas were the intellectuals, the ruling class who made the laws and provided the teachers and priests. Next Kshatriyas, the warrior and King class, whose duty it was to uphold the Law and protect the people (Arjuna of the Gita was of this class). The Naishyas were the Merchant class, whose duty it was to provide, to buy and sell and so to create the wealth of the nation, but with due regard for honest trading and charity and to guard against avarice. Finally, lowest in the social scale were the labourers, the Shudras whose tasks were to be carried out actively and honestly, with loyalty to their employer in every respect.

Thus, the Dharma of each class was clearly defined, and it was accepted that each had earned entry to his particular state by the Karma of his previous lives.

The social groups (or Varnas as they were known) developed on the basis of an organised society, but it was inherent that each should perform the duty of his particular class, according to his station and stage, to the best of his ability and in a spirit of self-sacrifice.

In the Gita we read (3–9) "Except by work done as sacrifice, the world is in bondage to work. Therefore carry out thy work as a sacrifice, thus becoming free from the bondage of attachment."

In (3–8) "Do thou perform thy best in thy allotted work, for action is better than inaction. Even maintenance of thy body cannot be achieved without action."

(18–47) "Better one's own Svabhava (work) though imperfectly carried out, than the Svabhava of another perfectly done."

(3–35) "Better one's own Svadharma though imperfectly done. Better is death in one's own Svadharma, for to follow that of another is perilous."

These lines of the Gita are a clear warning against envy of another's station and possessions, for these are the individual rewards of earlier good deeds, they are a fulfilment of Karmic Law. If we wish to attain the same, we have only to apply ourselves in the right direction, and the Law will provide the fulfilment.

The Caste System has now almost disappeared, but the Philosophy of Yoga presents a series of four stages in man's life, through which he may proceed to Illumination. The four stages, sometimes referred to as "ashramas", are as follows:

Stage 1 The Student Stage – Brahmacharya
Stage 2 The Householder Stage – Garshastrya
Stage 3 The Retirement Stage – Varnaprastna
Stage 4 The Renunciation Stage – Sannyasa

The Yogic Path of Attainment begins when the mind is first opened to an awareness of man's spiritual nature, and one becomes impelled by an urge for deeper knowledge. One then enters the phase of studentship, when information is absorbed from books, lectures, discussions and experience. The Dharma of the Student is to attain knowledge which will fit him for life both materially and spiritually.

As one moves deeper into the "unknown", occult knowledge, which had such an eerie feeling of mystery about it previously, now appears to be no more than the application of normal physical laws; instead of physical science, we find that scientific laws of cause and effect have moved into the spiritual world (where, of course, they have always existed), to become "spiritual science", and, once we have become accustomed to the new language, we feel quite at home. Physical science is, in fact the manifestation of spiritual science.

Following the studentship phase, the married state is generally the next step, for marriage, apart from providing countless opportunities for fulfilment and expansion of the personality, provides also an excellent training ground for developing spiritual qualities.

The basis of Bhakta Yoga is Love and Self-sacrificing service, and in marriage both qualities can mature to a divine experience. The sexual aspect of marriage, given as an expression of love of which the fruit is happy, healthy children and a devoted family, carries with it an elevation of spirit, comparable to spiritual ecstasy. If indulged in for sensual pleasure only, its spiritual aspect is lost, and it becomes no more than the satisfaction of an appetite, in which man is on no higher level than a monkey.

Brahmacharya (celibacy in the married state as well as the student stage) is given as an ideal which must be aimed at, the married state therefore giving the opportunity for man to raise himself to the heights, or to cast himself down to the level of the beast. Yogi Philosophy provides the knowledge whereby man may control his lower instincts, sublimating his energies to creative powers, using them to feed mind and brain, so raising his consciousness to higher things, opening himself to the influence of the spirit rather than that of the beast.

The first duty of the householder in his married state is to achieve financial security by attaining to a profession or similar station in life in which he can adequately provide for his family, at the same time making himself free of economic worry so that he may apply himself to devotional activities and study of the Scriptures.

The first of these studies, apart from the Vedas and Upanishads, is usually Hatha Yoga, which, as well as giving him a healthy body and a keen mind, maintaining him a well-balanced individual in all respects and at all times, gives him those exercises which enable the development of the strict self-control required for further development. By means of the asanas, postures and mudras of Hatha Yoga, celibacy may be

achieved without undue strain, and with a heightening of
mental powers.

This is the Dharma of the Householder Stage. Having
established his family in security, it is common practice for the
householder, who by now will have travelled some way along
the Yogic Path, to leave home and family to take up residence
with his Guru, or to travel in search of knowledge and
experience. In this phase, the probationer visits various
ashrams, spending years in some and perhaps only weeks in
others, searching for the Guru who can lead him to final
initiation. Having achieved this and having become himself a
Yogi, he will then either return to the world to give his
knowledge and skill to alleviate the sorrows and sufferings of
sick humanity, or retire to forest or cave for further meditation
and self-development.

When an Indian leaves his home and family, putting on the
garb of a mendicant in his pursuit of truth and a Spiritual
Teacher, he may wander for some time, visiting ashram after
ashram, sitting at the feet of one Master after another, gleaning
knowledge from each, and attaining those spiritual gifts which
extend his wisdom and consciousness. He must undergo trials
and sufferings, by which he will grow in spiritual strength and
knowledge of himself. He will beg his food and deny himself any
possessions, learning daily to "live in God", trusting himself
entirely to the Father. Then, one day, he may find an inner urge
which sends him to a distant place, and there he will find the
Guru who has sent him that psychic message, and with him he
will live until his teaching is complete, and he has become Self
Realised, an initiate into the company of true Adepts.

He will then either remain in seclusion to attain further self-
perfection before using his now considerable mental powers in
helping mankind, or he will sacrifice his own desires to return to
the mundane and suffering world, to teach and to assist those in
need. It is one of the tenets of Yoga that those who travel the
Path must help those who follow on, even as they themselves
have been helped in the past. The analogy is given of a man who
climbs a mountain when, having struggled to the summit
through suffering and trial, he turns to give his hand to those
who follow, using his strength and wisdom to save them from
harm.

Edward Carpenter, a well-known writer of the late ninteenth

century, illustrates this point in his book, *A Visit to a Gnani*. He tells of Panjali Harana Sahib, a wealthy and influential relative of a certain Rajah, who, having studied the scriptures and received some enlightenment thereby, resolved to devote the rest of his life to the pursuit of knowledge and Self-Realisation. Although middle-aged, he quietly disappeared one day, telling his family that he was going on a railway journey. Instructing his servants to take his carriage from the Palace and saying that he would follow, Panjali Harana Sahib went off quietly, alone, and was never seen by his family again. His Guru, of course, knew of the man's whereabouts, but this remained a secret which has never been revealed, although it was known that the Sahib received initiation and went far in his attainments.

There was also the case of Tilleinathan, a wealthy merchant of good family, a devotee of Yoga for many years who finally reached the stage of initiation. At this point, the trivialities of temporal possessions and pleasures could no longer hold him. He then sold up his business, divided his possessions among his family and friends, and disappeared into the forest to live the life of a hermit and to search for knowledge. In spite of frequent appeals by his family, Tilleinathan never returned to his home, but, appearing from time to time in public in later years, established a reputation as a great Yogi and holy man.

In more recent times, Selvarajan Yesudian* relates how a friend of his family, a wealthy judge, widely known for his high principles and general goodness, when at the peak of a successful career, gave it all up to "seek the inner path of the soul". He put away his English-cut occidental clothes, exchanging them for the rags of a mendicant. "He took leave of my father with the following words: God bless you, my friend. I have done my duty here on earth as an honourable member of human society. Now I am going to seek the Bread of Life." Turning his back upon all the delusions of earthly joys and pleasures physical, he said goodbye to his dearly loved family and set out upon the inner pathway of the soul in the search for TRUTH. The world's illusions could satisfy him no longer, for they are temporary and mortal. He longed for the infinite, the immortal, the eternal. He had planted the seeds which God had given him; he had garnered the harvest for those he loved. Then he went through the gate to FREEDOM.

* *Yoga Uniting East and West*, published by Allen & Unwin.

As a final example, we may take the life of one who is still living, whose services to mankind have earned him veneration throughout India as a living saint, as well as appreciation by heads of State for the good effect his work is having in alleviating conditions among the poor and the homeless. His name is Vinaya Narhari Bhave, but he is more commonly known as Vinoba, and by the masses simply Baba-ji. He is now past his seventieth year, a slight, almost emaciated figure, clad only in thin cotton shawl over a homespun dhoti. His only possessions are a bundle of clothes and a small spinning wheel which he carries with him on his travels, in a box.

Vinoba was born in a village outside Bombay and has one sister and four brothers of whom he is the eldest. His Brahmin parents were known for their piety and charity, and his father was a technologist in the textile industry. Vinoba, we are told, showed unusual intelligence as a child, entering high school at the age of ten, and distinguishing himself particularly in the study of mathematics. It was planned that the boy would continue his education in Europe, but when only ten years old, Vinoba had already taken the vow of celibacy, and was deep in the study of the scriptures and spiritual matters.

It was no surprise to find that, when the time came for Vinoba to go to Bombay university he went to the mecca of all spiritual students in India, the holy city of Benares, there to seek his Guru and to pursue the inner path. He later became the disciple of Mahatma Ghandi, joining him at Ahmedabad, where he vowed to abstain from the use of salt, and to wear only one garment for the rest of his life. Vinoba's success at the Kochrab Ashram may be judged by Ghandi's remark that he was "the finest jewel of the ashram, the most noble soul I have ever met".

For thirty-five years Vinoba travelled from one ashram to another in search of knowledge and self-perfection. His constantly reiterated prayer was his "earnest desire that God will make me an instrument of service to Him". As a result he spent and is still spending the rest of his life in the service of the poor, carrying out whatever tasks and labours were necessary for their welfare.

His real mission received its first impulse in 1951, when he arrived at Telengana in the old princely state of Hyderabad. Here he saw the terrible conditions in which thousands of the poor and homeless were trying to survive. When India gained her Independence, some ninety per cent of the population lived in villages under a feudal system operated by the landowners. This system was abolished, and Tenancy Acts were passed to alleviate conditions of the exploited and unprotected poor. The immediate result of this was to expose the unfortunates to the wiles of Communism on the one hand, and extortionate demands from the landlords on the other. Into this vortex of violence and vicious rapacity stepped Vinoba, shocked and sorely distressed by the misery he saw. Visiting a colony of harijans (families of low-caste poor), Vinoba asked how much land they would need for their accommodation and sustenance. He was told "Eighty acres".

What followed then, is now a matter of recorded history, a small event which is still "snowballing" its effects across the face of India. Vinoba closed his eyes for a moment in prayer, then asked, "Is it possible that any landlord would donate land to cure the misery, the poverty and the unemployment in this village?" There was an awed silence in which doubt and disbelief were mingled, when suddenly, Sri V. Ramachandre Reddy, a local leading landlord, rose to his feet and exclaimed, "I will donate one hundred acres of land." With these words the great "Bhoodan Movement" was born, for a committee was immediately formed to arrange the distribution of the land and to obtain the necessary agricultural implements, seed and bullocks, wherewith it might be cultivated.

Vinoba, overjoyed and encouraged by the success of his plea, spent the following night in prayer, asking for Divine assistance to help him touch the hearts of other landlords in other places in the same way, so that the plight of the unfortunate harijans could be appeased on a national scale. The next day he moved on to another village, where he collected donations amounting to a further ninety acres of land, and so Vinoba's Mission had begun. From this point he has since travelled a distance of more than 15,000 miles since 1951, and as one report puts it* "His bed is often the bare ground. Neither sickness nor floods deter him; he will tramp eleven miles in a morning though suffering from fever, and will wade knee-deep through water to reach his beloved poor."

Thus was the Bhoodan (land gift) Movement born. It is now flourishing as Vinoba and his helpers move from village to

---

* B. Jayagree, Vitayawada.

village, always on foot, always identifying themselves with the poor and keeping nothing for themselves. The Movement has no well-appointed office, no large house in sequestered isolation, for every single donation goes straight to the needs of the poor, being administered by their own local community. In the first four years the Movement has distributed almost four million acres of land among some 57,000 families, taking not one anna for their own reward.

It is no wonder then, that Ghandi named Vinoba the "jewel of the ashram" that Pandit Nehru referred to Vinoba as "a rock of strength in these troubled times", whilst Dr. Radhakrishnen openly stated that, "we are fortunate in having this great soul who is calling us to action for the sake of the suffering millions of India".

Vinoba's technique has never varied. He knows now, that his simple and sincere prayer has been answered, that he is God's instrument in the great work of helping the poor and the homeless. His simple philosophy is that the earth belongs to no man, but is the property of God alone, who is its Creator; no man can truly "own" a piece of land, he can only order its destiny. Vinoba appeals to the landowners that, "God stands before you in the form of the poor and the homeless", that all are brothers in the sight of God, that it is the privilege of the wealthy to help their less fortunate brothers.

In the life of Vinoba, one can see the highest teachings of Yogi Philosophy fulfilled in every way, for Vinoba first gave up all he had to follow the inner path, spent many years as a student of the scriptures and spiritual life under the guidance of his Guru, finally devoting the rest of his life to the cause of the poor and homeless. "Seek and ye shall find." "Ask and ye shall receive." In Vinoba we can see these promises fulfilled, even as they will be fulfilled for any man if he has but Faith and Sincerity.

CHAPTER 11

Realisation – The Inner Knowledge

The reader is probably fully aware, by now, of what is meant by "Realisation". One dictionary defines this as "to make real", but our form of Realisation is the achievement of unity with a Reality which already exists, "The Ultimate Reality".

To achieve Self-Realisation is to meet one's true Spiritual Self in full consciousness whilst still in the flesh, and to know that on that plane only – the Spiritual Plane – lies the true Reality.

Such a statement may sound altogether too glib for the average western mind, accustomed as it is to dealing with demonstrable facts in a logical manner. But scientific proof of the illusory nature of this world already exists. We have only to think beyond superficial appearances to agree with the conclusion of the Yogi that the physical world is "Maya" – an illusion.*

The simplest proof lies in the smallest things – the atoms of which the material world is made, for as every schoolchild now knows, the electrons, protons and neutrons which comprise an atom, are in themselves "concentrated vortices of energy" or "an aura surrounding a cavity". In the ultimate analysis therefore they are no more tangible than electricity whose manifestation can be clearly perceived but the thing itself remains invisible.

Our sense perceptions tell us only what exists over a very restricted area of events, whether these be in terms of sight, sound or touch. The electromagnetic scale of vibration for example extends for a considerable span on both sides of our own narrow band of perceptions.

If we trace through the scale to the higher range of vibrations it is seen that the vibrations become more and more rapid until

* See *Yoga The Key to Life*.

they disappear into the fourth dimension, where, although our dormant psychic senses could respond, our normal, physical perceptions are useless.

Hence, by extrapolation and inference, comes the vision of a great Central Power from which all vibrations (and therefore all creation) emanates. Seers and saints of all castes and creeds have borne witness to it, calling the Central Power by many different names such as God, Universal Creator, Universal Mind and so on, but all, fundamentally, say the same thing, even though different words are used.

A further point is that the Great Creator is universal, eternal and unchanging so that, compared with what is limited, temporary, and always undergoing change, the Creator must be regarded as the true Reality.

The concept of Maya arises in that man is generally inclined to think of the Real as being only that which can be seen to be proved, and he remains therefore in a state of ignorance which shields from him the Reality which is true, unchanging and eternal, but of a subtle nature imperceptible to our senses.

It is the function of Yoga to remove the ignorance and to provide the practices whereby man is made able to know the True Reality the Real Self, that is, to achieve "Self-Realisation".

Another concept of the Philosophy which frequently provides a stumbling block to the beginner, is the concept of the "One in the Many", the "All is One".

If we relate all things to One Creator, then, if, before the act of Creation there was nothing, and the universe as we know it did not exist, then all Creation must have emanated from the Creator Himself, for nothing else existed wherefrom creation could be fabricated.

We can now bring together two facts which open the way to further understanding.

First, we now know that matter only appears to be solid because our sense perceptions of touch and sight tell us so. But science has proved that all matter is composed of atoms, which, in the ultimate analysis are vortices of energy which have no substance at all. What we *do* know is that different substances have different atomic weights and different natural rates of vibration.

This brings us to our second point which is that every

chemical element has its own specific frequency of vibration. It begins with the natural vibration rate of "solids" and moves then through liquids and gases into the electromagnetic range, which takes us far beyond the range of sense perception, and onward even further to a point where science cannot provide instruments which are fine enough to respond.

We have moved then into the fourth dimension, the Plane of Mind. But occultists know that the finer bodies of the etheric and astral also have their natural rate of vibration, and that the frequencies of vibration go on increasing through the mental plane to the very Spirit itself.

Therefore the whole of Creation can be seen as a vast Primal Energy which radiates from the Primal Source in the form of rays, each having different rates of vibration and so creating different Planes and different substances. Each Plane can be seen as a different band of frequencies like the radio wavebands on radio sets.

This Primal Energy is called Prana, and all forms of energy, all forces, are but different forms of Prana.

The basic substance of the universe is etherial and is called Akasa. Matter is formed by Prana acting upon Akasa.

To see this more clearly a simple analogy has been drawn between the One in the act or Creation, and the action of white light or passing through a prism. (See Fig. 12, page 156.)

It is easy to see, now, why all the Scriptures emphasise the need for physical and mental purification as a first step, for if our bodies are gross and heavy as a result of coarse foods and coarse living, then one's mind cannot possibly open to the finer vibration of the Higher Planes. We simply remain as animals.

Having refined the body then refinement of mind must follow, for it is reiterated throughout Yogi Philosophy, time after time after time, that unless we exercise discrimination and self-control, we will remain chained to the physical world for all time, either in our physical body or in the world hereafter.

The binding chains are forged from the links of desires in the heat of passion, and the longer these are allowed to exist, the stronger will be the chain, the more securely will we be bound, and the happiness of Spiritual Life which "passeth all understanding", could never then be ours.

We can now summarise the principal tenets upon which the

Philosophy stands, each of which is worthy of deep meditation, each of which can be a guiding principle on the Path of Attainment, the Way to Self-Realisation:

First Principle.　　There is only one Divine Creator, the Absolute God – head from whence the Universe and all it contains, emanates.

Second Principle.　　The One Creator is unmanifest, eternal, immutable, omnipresent, all-pervading, neuter. He is at once the Creator, Sustainer and Destroyer of all that exists.

Third Principle.　　Man, in his essence, is a Spiritual Being. He is a soul incarnated in a body. The Soul is already existent and not something which has to be striven for. It is eternal.

Fourth Principle.　　All life has a purpose, which is to manifest that within itself which is Divine.

Fifth Principle.　　Manifestation by Self-Realisation can be achieved by every human being by orientating one's Self to the Spirit and living life to the dictates of Spirit and not the dictates of animal.

Sixth Principle.　　Until man has liberated himself from the bondage of the flesh, he will be reborn in order to obtain correction.

Seventh Principle.　　The corrective power which operates as a Universal Law is Karma, the Law of Cause and Effect.

Eighth Principle.　　When man has achieved perfection, he becomes united with the absolute, to remain eternally in a state of bliss and enlightenment.

These, then, are the Principles on which Yogi Philosophy stands and which summarise the teachings of Sacred Literature.

The Vedas, the Upanishads and the Gita expound the theological teaching (in addition, of course, to the rituals and hymns), whilst the practical teaching which give the ways and means whereby one may attempt to achieve perfection, were given by Patanjali, by the many Gurus through the ages, and by those passages in the Gita dealing with the Yogas.

The Philosophy is therefore complete, in that it gives far-reaching knowledge which embraces the physical, mental and spiritual planes of life, and also tells how advancement on each plane may be achieved. Furthermore, with respect to ideals and actions, it not only tells precisely why some are "right" and others "wrong" but also the resulting reactions of each. Therefore we are told clearly WHY we should use our best endeavour to travel the Path to Attainment. (To do otherwise is surely a waste of life.)

All religions have Commandments which must be observed in order to attain to Spiritual Life, for example the Ten Commandments of Christianity. Yoga has no Commandments as such, but has its several different schools (Hatha, Bhakta, Raja, Jnana, Karma), which give the necessary teaching and practices which lead to Purification and Self-control.

The nearest approach to actual Commandments are the Eight Limbs of Yoga, given by Patanjali in Aphorism II/29. These Eight Limbs are in themselves a complete course of mental and physical training and may be elaborated as follows:*

FIRST LIMB – YAMA – gives the 5 abstinences as

   i Abstaining from injury to others.
  ii Abstaining from lying.
 iii Abstaining from theft.
 iv Abstaining from incontinence.
  v Abstaining from greed.

These have been further elaborated in the practice of Yoga by the Ten Rules of Conduct, which are

   i Non-injury of others by physical violence, uncharitable comment, gossip.
  ii To see truth and to tell truth in all things regardless of consequence. To practise Discrimination in speech and action, to discern truth from falsehood.
 iii Respect of other's property (including good name and reputation) and to abstain from any form of theft.
 iv To practise continence and chastity (Brahmacharya) in thought, word and deed.
  v To practise tolerance and understanding, forgiveness and to forgo thoughts of vengeance.

* See also *Yoga The Key to Life*.

  vi To practise patience, forbearance, long-suffering endurance and obedience.

 vii To exercise compassion and sympathy for the poor, the weak and the afflicted.

viii To be sincere in all things and to exercise earnest endeavour, accepting responsibility and fulfilling duties.

  ix To live and eat with circumspection, having neither too much nor too little in every respect.

   x To develop a strong body and a strong will, practising hygiene and purity of body and mind.

SECOND LIMB – NIYAMA – the 5 observances

   i Purification.
  ii Contentment.
 iii Control.
  iv Study.
   v Attentiveness to God.

Yoga elaborates these into the Ten Rules of CONTROL as follows:

   i To achieve purification by purging out adverse Karma. This involves retribution for wrongs committed and the practice of penance as a form of retribution.

  ii Acceptance of the Dharma to which we are born, to be content to live with that inner peace which Knowledge and Devotion will bring.

 iii Faith in the Laws of God, which ensure our continued progress, always to a better state, through all eternity.

  iv Control of thoughts, words and actions.

   v Veneration of all things holy, and Worship of God.

  vi Study of sacred scriptures and literature, attending discussions on spiritual matters, attending lectures which will deepen Self-Knowledge and dispel Maya.

 vii Control of Pride and Egotism and practice of their opposite virtues.

viii Control of mental powers and to pursue their development.

  ix To practise daily prayer and meditation.

   x To control selfishness, bigotry and narrow-mindedness, and to practise self-sacrifice in helping others.

The second chapter of Patanjali (II/34–48) comments upon

the rewards to be obtained by following the injunctions of Yama and Niyama.

THIRD LIMB – ASANAS

These are the movements and postures taught in Hatha Yoga. Their purpose is to purify, strengthen and to develop the concentration and mind power necessary in the practice of Raja Yoga.*

FOURTH LIMB – PRANAYAMA

This could be called the "Science of Breath" (upon which Yogi Ramacharaka has written a very useful booklet, published by Fowler). The importance of Prana (the Absolute Energy) in the support of life has already been discussed and as Prana exists in its greatest abundance in the air we breathe, correct breathing is seen to be essential to good health.

Breathing techniques are also associated with body control, emotional control, and mental control, and their knowledge and practice is therefore clearly essential.*

Patanjali's Aphorisms II/49–55 deal with the control of breath.

FIFTH LIMB – PRATYAHARA

Withdrawal of the senses. By concentrating the mind inward, sense reaction to external stimuli (and internal body activity) is gradually withdrawn, so that full consciousness can be applied to mind activity. "In consequence," says Patanjali (II/52), "the covering of the light is dissolved."

SIXTH LIMB – DHARANA – Concentration

In the practice of concentration the mind is brought to one point and held there in concentration. The resulting concentrated energy may then be directed to body control, or to holding the mind one-pointed for a period. As in the Mundaka Upanishad, the mind may be likened to an arrow ". . . the arrow is the Atman (the Self). Brahman is the mark of the arrow the aim of the soul."

In *The Cloud of Unknowing* (author unknown) the arrow is the mind which is to be directed against the dark cloud of

* For detailed description see *Yoga The Key to Life*.

"unknowing". When the cloud has been pierced then the Divine Light is seen.

SEVENTH LIMB – DHYANA – Meditation

With the mind held in concentration upon a thing or subject, thoughts begin to flow in unbroken succession. Where such state of uninterrupted flow takes place, a condition of meditation exists.

One Yogic practice is to imagine the thing or subject as being contained in the centre of a circle, and thoughts are held within the circle and so concentrated on the subject of the meditation.

EIGHTH LIMB – SAMADHI – Contemplation

As a natural sequence of events, the flow of mind in meditation passes into a state of contemplation, when the mind and object become one. If the subject of meditation is Divine, then a state of Bliss develops and the Self becomes transcendent. It is in this state that super-sensible knowledge is arrived at.

Patanjali summarises the final three Limbs in Ahphorisms III/1–5 as follows:

III/1   Dharana is holding the mind steady on one thing or object
III/2   Dhyana occurs when there is an unbroken flow of knowledge (thought)
III/3   Samadhi exists when the object of meditation alone exists and all awareness of self disappears.
III/4   These three together constitute the practice of Samyama when applied to one object.
III/5   By mastery of Samyama all knowledge comes to light.

Patanjali also gives fair warning that (III/6) "Such mastery is only obtained by steps."

The Eight Limbs of Yoga can now be seen as one of the most important concepts of the whole Philosophy of Yoga. With a remarkable economy of words, Patanjali has practically summarised all that is necessary, from the veriest beginner to the most advanced Sanyasi, to achieve all-knowledge and unity with the Divine.

The Eight Limbs can be seen as a step-ladder from the dawning of the awareness of the "I AM" to the final stages of Mastery and Transcendence. Fig. 13 illustrates the point. This

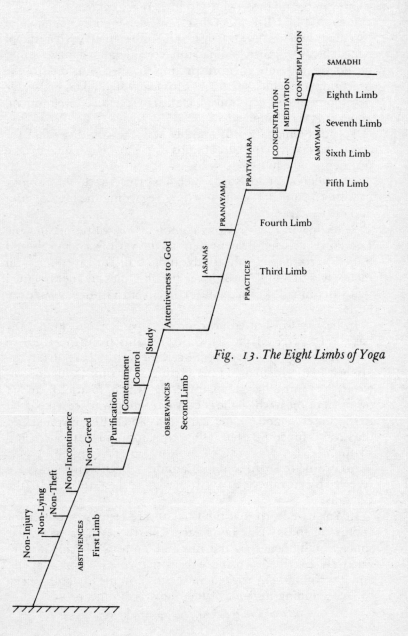

Fig. 13. The Eight Limbs of Yoga

SAMADHI

CONTEMPLATION

Eighth Limb

MEDITATION

Seventh Limb

CONCENTRATION

SAMYAMA

Sixth Limb

PRATYAHARA

Fifth Limb

PRANAYAMA

Fourth Limb

ASANAS

PRACTICES

Third Limb

Attentiveness to God

Study

Control

Contentment

Purification

OBSERVANCES

Second Limb

Non-Greed

Non-Incontinence

Non-Theft

Non-Lying

Non-Injury

ABSTINENCES

First Limb

sketch serves to illustrate also the essential preliminary steps (First and Second Limbs) which must be observed before the Third Limb, and those which follow are attempted.

It should be self-evident that if one achieved the mental and psychic powers given by Yoga, but still retained early traits of lying, cheating, greed and passion, considerable damage could be done, not only to unsuspecting victims, but also to the practitioner. Steiner's tenet that for every step taken in psychic development two steps must be taken in spiritual development, appears as very sound advice.

To put Steiner's words another way, we could say that for every step taken in the latter Limbs of Yoga, it is essential to take two steps in the first two Limbs.

Another concept of Yoga which has proved a stumbling block to western students, is the teaching regarding the human aura and the Chakras.

Reverting to our previous comments on vibration and the Life Force it is self-evident that, as the various chemicals and minerals comprising the body and its organs are lifeless in themselves (if a limb or organ is cut off it dies and decays) then that sustaining Life Force must come from a source outside the body.

In Fig. 12 we showed how the Creative Force of Prana, the basic Life Force of the Universe, streams from the Creative Centre, giving life energy to all creatures. In passing from the Higher Plane to man, Prana, acting in a similar manner to electricity, must have a path along which to travel, and a terminal point at which the energy is received whence it is passed to specific areas and organs of the body and there converted into the various functions of heat digestion, movement, thought and so on.

According to Dr Alexander Cannon,* the life-giving rays are received by the Etheric Body, from whence they are passed to the Chakras.

In Yoga we learn that the Chakras are centres of power (or energy) in the psychic body each Chakra having a particular sphere of influence in the physical body. The Chakras are variously described as being "wheel-shaped" or "lotus shaped" and it is common in Yoga literature to show the Chakras as seen by one standing in front of the body. From this position they

---

* *The Shadow of Destiny*, published by Rider & Co.

appear as flat discs. Leadbetter of the Theosophical Society shows them as viewed from the side, which gives a more realistic view. Seen from this poistion the Chakras appear to be flower-shaped, so that a western clairvoyant would compare the shape to that of a lily, whereas an oriental would compare the shape to the lotus, with which he would be more familiar.

It appears to be the function of the Chakras to receive energy, subtle and refined according to those functions to which it gives life. This energy is absorbed by the Chakras and channelled to those parts and organs it controls.

The Chakras differ in form and colour, the form being varied by the number of "petals" which appear around a central circle or disc. Each "petal" has its own shade of colour, and if we now relate colour to vibration, it can be seen that the main "carrier ray" to each Chakra, is broken up into components, each of which serves a specific part of a specific Chakra.

Referring to Fig. 14 in which the Chakras and their life-giving rays are shown, it can be seen that starting from the Root Chakra, the Muladhara, the number of "petals", and therefore the number of "sub-rays", increases as the position of the Chakra is higher in the body, inferring a greater complexity of purpose and function.

To clarify this, we may table the Chakras and their description as follows:

Name	Number of Petals	Location	Area of Influence	Associated Colour
Muladhara	4	Pelvis	Regenerative organs and evacuation	Red
Svadisthara	6	Abdomen	Intestines and stomach	Orange
Manipura	10	Solar plexus	Solar plexus, diaphragm	Yellow
Anahata	12	Chest	Heart and lungs	Green
Vishuddha	16	Neck	Throat and thyroids	Grey-blue
Ajna	2	Eyebrows	Mouth and face	Indigo
Sahasrara	"1000"	Centre of crown	Scalp and eyes	White

A significant contribution from Science has been made by researcher Dr. Wilhelm Reich, whose experiments showed that the body can be divided into seven segments (or zones of influence) each segment being formed by a circular zone around the body.

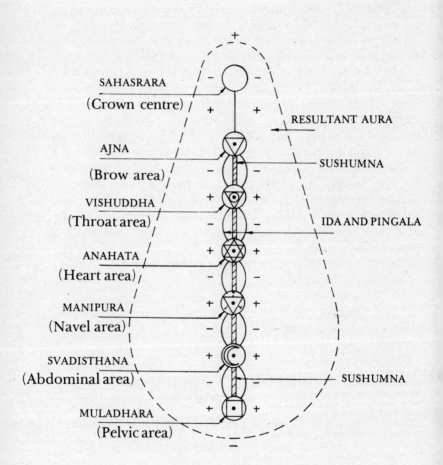

Fig. 14. Chakras and aura

It needs little imagination to associate Dr. Reich's Seven Zones with Yoga's Seven Chakras.

The Kundalini Power (Shakti) is said to reside in the Root Chakra – the Muladhara and concentration upon any particular Chakra stimulates action in that area of influence so that concentration on the Muladhara, accompanied by certain specified asanas, mudras and bandhas, results in arousing the "Sleeping Serpent" or the Kundalini Shakti as it is generally known.

We now have a picture of Divine Life flowing into the body, where this energy is converted into the many physical and mental processes and functions of that complex organisation.

We know also that the nervous system through which the energy passes, acts in a similar manner to an electrical circuit. Also, similarly to an electrical current, each section and organ of the body gives off vibrations which are consequent upon the energy flowing through it.

Inasmuch as all electrical conductors have a magnetic field associated with them, which is generated by the electric current passing through, a similar field is associated with the various parts and organs of the body.

The resultant "field" around the body constitutes what is known as the human "aura" which can be seen by clairvoyants, who tell us that all living forms have an associated aura, and that the state of the aura discloses the mental and physical states of the individual.*

Thus we see the system of creation and the support of life as being a system of Creative Force streaming into the universe from the Divine Centre.

From the two fundamental concepts of Absolute Energy (Prana) and Absolute Substance (Akasa) the whole universe and all it contains is constructed in descending degrees of refinement from the spiritual to the psychic (or mental) plane, from the psychic to the physical where again we see creation in descending orders of refinement.

The message of Yoga is that man is an essential part of the whole which he inhabits on three co-existent planes, the spiritual, the psychic and the physical.

Within man himself, therefore we see again the descending order of refinement, and the Philosophy of Yoga contains all the

* See also Appendix II.

knowledge necessary to show how man may reach within himself to meet and unite with the Divine Self, so that he may attain to all-knowledge and perfect bliss to become one with the Infinite.

In his book *The Shadow of Destiny* (published by Rider & Co.), Dr. Alexander Cannon reports a discussion between a certain Dr. Hensoldt and a Yogi named Coomra Sami during Dr. Hensoldt's investigations into occult phenomena in India. The doctor spent some six months with Coomra Sami in which "he witnessed manifestations of the wonderful powers possessed by this great Adept".

In saying his farewells to Dr. Hensoldt, the Adept spoke to him as follows: "The Path lies everywhere and nowhere, and the eternal truth you must seek for within the depths of your own consciousness. There is no royal road to success and you must climb to the heights by your own efforts. I was once as you are now, and I well remember the impatience and the madness of despair which overwhelmed me more than once, as I realised the stupendousness of the task before me; how my heart almost failed me, and how, more than once, I was on the point of giving up the battle. Wealth, ease, luxury and all the delusive pleasures which hold man in bondage, I had abandoned, and had almost completely subdued and mastered the evil propensities of animality with which our race is afflicted. Yet such is the demon of perversity, inherited all-powerful from the past, that it required all the fierce determination of which I am capable, to persist in the upward path.

"'Through the night to the light' should be your motto in this course of ascent. The greater the obstacles, the greater the triumph, and though seclusion is to be recommended under all circumstances, if you are the right calibre you will succeed whoever you are.

"We Hindus are a race immeasurably older in mental culture than the western races. Your so-called civilisation is but of yesterday and you are merely engaged in an unending process of multiplying your wants. You have abnormally developed and stimulated the accumulative instinct, so that you have come to look upon life as a mere opportunity of piling up rubbish in the shape of material possessions. The luxuries of today become the necessities of tomorrow, and the greater the extent of those wants, the more you will have to toil to gratify them. You are forced to devote an ever-increasing part of your life to procuring the means whereby these artificial wants may be gratified. You are indeed a slave of your wants, for each want implies a new sorrow inasmuch as sorrow is experienced in deprivation of the means of gratification. A thousand wants mean a thousand sorrows, a thousand disappointments a thousand pains.

"Has the standard of happiness been raised in the slightest degree by your much-valued civilisation?

"I say no. On the contrary, you suffer more than your forefathers did at any time, because they lived in a simple, more frugal manner, and their wants were fewer.

"We Hindus on the other hand, after having reached a certain stage of material culture we have paused, reflected and have reduced our wants to a minimum. All our wants, translated into time, would mean less than 20 minutes work each day. We can devote all the remainder of our time to mental culture – that is to thinking, not to book-study, but to the solution of the world mystery. We have developed during the last fifty centuries mind-faculties which are a source of constant surprise to you. In fact while you have been working for your stomach, we have been working for our brain."

The Yogi therefore points to the Path as being one of difficulty, but one in which all may triumph in the end. The desire for possessions is emphasised as the thing to be avoided, the thing which binds man to the lower elements and denies to him his real heritage.

Although we may find Coomra Sami's criticism of the west a trifle harsh we can see therein the path to be followed, and clearly one must remember at all times:

"THOU ART THAT"

The Work of Dr. Harold S. Burr

The concept of a completely unified universe, in which every single thing is inter-related and inter-acted upon, is new to many and is still quite unacceptable to some.

Occultists tell us that we have now entered the age of Aquarius in which man's mental and psychic aspects will become more active, more receptive to things of the Spirit rather than to things of the flesh, and much of what has previously been known as "occult mystery" or "Ancient wisdom" will be made known to all seekers.

It is true to say that there has never been such a universal interest in psychic matters. E.S.P., telepathy, clairvoyance, astrology, spiritual healing, psychic phenomena of all kinds are in the forefront of interest today, whereas, even a few years ago, any reference to psychic phenomena, any interest shown in this or allied subjects, were taken to be the signs of a crank.

Now, however, with the advent of electronics, whose technology has advanced at a fantastic rate in the last decade, practical proof is forthcoming from scientists, physicists, biologists and bio-chemists, that the real world, the world from which our own emanates, is sustained and is organised, in the world of what has previously been known as "occult".

Modern instruments, coupled with modern knowledge and technologies, have proved conclusively, beyond all doubt, that another, subtle world exists of which we are a closely integrated part, and that all things in the universe inter-act and react upon each other.

To my mind, one of the most important discoveries of this age (in respect of the questions "who am I, what am I") has been made by Dr. Harold S. Burr, Ph.D., of the Yale University School of Medicine.

For nearly forty years, Dr. Burr and his associates have

experimented on the electric fields which surround and organise the human body.

Dr. Burr's researches have provided positive, tangible evidence of the electro-dynamic fields which permeate the universe, and which form the physical pattern of all living things.

Developing his own instruments, Dr. Burr has traced the "Life Fields" and the "Thought Fields" by which the body is controlled, but has gone even further to prove that these, again, are acted upon by cosmic fields which exist and function throughout the universe.

It is now some years since Dr. Kilner of St. Thomas Hospital, London, similarly proved the existence of the human aura. Dr. Burr has now shown that the entire universe exists within a similar "field" of electro-magnetic energy.

Therefore it becomes possible, now, to demonstrate factually that "All is One", that life has meaning and purpose, and that man is an integral part of the universe in which he lives.

It is also possible to show how mind and body are related, not only to themselves, but to similar organisms and that E.S.P., telekinesis, telepathy, clairvoyance, spiritual healing, respond to physical laws and are every bit as real as the electric light which responds to the touch of a switch.

It is hoped to correlate these important facts and findings in a further book, in which it will also be seen that the "ancient wisdom" and the Philosophy of Yoga, have known for thousands of years, what is only now being proved by science.

J. McCartney

APPENDIX II

The Seven Principles of Man and the Aura

The Seven Principles or Planes upon which Man operates may be restated in the following form:

Plane 7 The Absolute Divine
Plane 6 The Causal Plane
Plane 5 The Intuitional (Inspirational) Plane
Plane 4 The Higher Mental Plane
Plane 3 The Lower Mental Plane
Plane 2 The Astral/Etheric and Life Force
Plane 1 The Physical Plane

Plane 1 Aura   Radiates from the Chakras in straight lines (which indicates a state of health) or drooping lines (sickness). It is the resultant of the etheric/astral forces, showing a pale red when healthy.

Plane 2 Aura   Extends about 12″ from the astral body which it encircles. It varies in colour and strength with the emotions which generate it, varying similarly with the quality of thought.

Plane 3 Aura   Is generated by both objective and subjective mental processes, so reflecting the intelligence and development of the individual.

Plane 4 Aura   The strength of this aura indicates the degree of artistic and cultural development of the individual, on the Plane of Inspiration.

Plane 5 Aura

Plane 6 Aura   Approaching the Spiritual Plane, this aura shows an etherial blue. It is the seat of all impressions and recorded experience (Sanskaras), and of the Causal Principle which permeates and reacts upon all the lower Planes. It only appears in highly developed souls.

Plane 7 Aura This appears as a band of brilliant light around the perimeter of the aura, but is generated only by the most highly developed Adepts and Masters, therefore is a very rare occurrence.

It may be noted that all the above Auras are generated internally, but the Spiritual Principle descends, entering as pure white light and bringing Life Force to the Human Organism.

A Glossary of Sanskrit

with a

Guide to Pronunciation

APPROXIMATE PRONUNCIATION OF
SANSKRIT LETTERS

VOWELS

a as in sam
â as in psalm
i as in knit
î as in neat
ri as in fiery
li as in friendly

u as in full
û as in fool
e as in date
ai as in aisle
o as in note
au as in proud

CONSONANTS

(a) Gutturals
K as in kite
Kh as in inkhorn
g as in gate
gh as in springhead
ṅ as in sing
h as in hear

(b) Palatals
k as in church
kh as in church-history
g as in jolly
gh as in bridge-house
ñ as in new
y as in yet
s as in sharp

(c) Dentals
t as in tin
th as in lanthorn
d as in din
dh as in landholder
n as in nay
l as in let
s as in grass

(d) Linguals
t as in town
th as in outhouse
d as in done
dh as in rodhook
n as in no
r as in red
sh as in shun

(e) Labials

p as in pan
ph as in topheavy
b as in bed
bh as in clubhouse
m as in mill
v as in live
m as in annul (slight nasal)
h as in sanga (slight breathing)

(With acknowledgements to Professor M. Muller and Oxford
University Press)

abhyāsa. Perseverance in Yoga or spiritual practice
abhyudaya. Exaltation
acharuana. A mouthwash
achara. Immobile
achara. Common custom
Achārya. Exalted teacher of spiritual truths
adharma. Sacrilegious behaviour
adhikara vāda. The doctrine of personal discipline or an acceptable
    student
adhishthātri devata. A presiding deity
adhyāsa. Confusion of identity
Ādhitya. A Hindu Deity
adrishta. Unknown – unseen – the subtle potential karmic cause
Advaita varda. Non-dualism in respect of Divine Unity
agami Karma. Current works
Āgama. Tantric texts
Agni. Fire (Agni-hotra – the Fire Ritual)
ahamta. The concept of "I"
ahamkara. The ego
ahimsa. Non-injury
aishwara. Spiritual (occult) power
ajapa. Involuntary repetition
ājñā. The chakra between the eyebrows
ajnana. Ignorance
ākāsha. The subtle etheric element
ākāsha vani. A spiritual voice
ākyāna. Allegory
alasya. Idleness
ambara. A covering
anādi. Uncreated – with no beginning
anadi Kala. The beginning of time

anāhata dhwani. A subtle sound heard in contemplation

anāhata. The heart chakra

ānanda. Bliss

ānanda-maya kosha. One of five sheaths surrounding the soul

anga. One of the eight limbs of Yoga

annamaya kosha. The physical sheath

antahkarana. The subtle instruments of sense — the entire mental process

antarayamin. God as the Inner Ruler

ap. The water element

apāna. The vital air operating downward in the pelvic area

apara. Of lower order

aparigraha. Abstinence from greed — one of the ten yamas

Aparā Prakriti. The cosmic energy through which living things are manifested

Arjuna. The warrior Prince of the Gita

artha. Wealth

Āryas. Indo Aryans

Arya dharma. The creed and duties of the Aryas

āsana. A Yoga posture

āshrama. One of the four stages of life (student, householder, retirement, monk)

Ashtanga Yoga. The Eight Limbs of Yoga

ashmiri. A mudra

asmita. Egotism — a cause of sorrow

ashubha. Evil

athara. Good conduct

atindriya. Beyond sense perception

Ātma Jnana. Knowledge of the Self

Ātman. The Self

atyantika pralaya. Apparent dissolution of the universe in contemplation

avarana. The veil of ignorance

Avatara. A Divine Incarnation

avidya. The quality of ignorance

awagaman. Continuous birth and death

Āyurveda. Medical science

baddha. A condition of bondage

bala. Strength — power — a paramita

bandha. A muscular lock (as in the chin lock)

bandhana. Bondage

basti. Internal cleansing

Bauddha. That which is Buddhist

Bhagavān. A spiritually realised person

bhajana. Hymn
Bhakta. A follower of Bhakti Yoga
Bhakti Yoga. The Yoga of Devotion
bakya karanas. External instruments of action
bhastrikā. The bellows motion in the Yoga breathing exercise
bhāva. Attitude or relationship
bhāvana. Holding an idea in the mind
bhoga. Sensual pleasure
bhuda. Separation
bhuta(s). Manifested element(s) of earth (ether, fire, air and water)
bhujāngāsana. The "Cobra" asan
Bhuma. Brahman as the "Unconditioned Infinite"
bhuvar loka. The sphere above the earth
bindu. A point
bhodi. Knowledge of the Supreme
Brahman. God as the Absolute
Brahmā. God as Creator
Brahmadwāra. The opening (door) in the spine where Kundalini enters
Brahmavidya. Knowledge of the Absolute
Brahmacharya. Celibacy – the first stage of ashrama
Brahmaloka. The sphere of Brahma
Brāhmana. The part of the Vedas which elucidates Vedic Hymns
Brahmānda. The total universe, subtle and physical
buddhi. Intellectual function of the mind

Chakra(s). Psychic centres (wheels) placed along the spine
Chaintanya. Pure Consciousness
chakshu. The subtle organ (indriya) of sight
chara. Able to move
chit. The absorption of subject and object in which full knowledge
    occurs
chitta. The subtle element of mind (mind stuff)
chitta shuddi. Purification of the chitta
chikrini. A subtle nerve running within the spinal column

daiva vārni. Spiritual voice heard in contemplation
daksha. Expertise
dāna. Offering a gift – the act of giving – generosity (a paramita)
darshana. Being in the presence of a holy person
Devaloka. The plane or sphere of the Devas (Deitys)
Devatā. A female Deity
dhāranā. The process of concentration, meditation and contemplation
dhāranurāsana. The "Bow" asan
dharma. The essence of a thing – duty – vocation – law
dhwani. A resonant sound

dhyāna. Meditation – a part of dharana – a paramita
dikshā. Initiation
dikshita. An initiate
drashtā. The observer
Durgā. The Absolute in the form of Divine Mother
Dvaita vāda. Dualism
dwesha. Antagonistic

ekagrata. One pointedness of mind

Ganapati. A Hindu deity
gandha. Smell
gārhasthya. The householder stage of life (āshrama)
gauni. Secondary or indirect
Gāyatri. A mantra sacred to Brahmins
ghata. The body as a vessel
ghi. Clarified butter
ghomukhāsana. The "Cow" asan
guna. A quality existing in all things (Satwa, Rajas, Tamas)
Guru. A Spiritual Teacher
granthis. The three "bindings", ignorance, desire and selfishness

Hiranyagarbha. A Hindu deity
hridaya. The heart

iccha. Desires
Ida. The left hand subtle nerve channel exterior to the spine and operating in conjunction with Pingala (the right hand channel)
idam. "This" as opposed to "That"
Indra. A Hindu deity
indriyas. Sense organs of the subtle body
Isha. A form of Shiva
ishta. A personal ideal to which one aspires
ishta nishthā. Self-sacrificing devotion to an ideal
ishta devata. Devotion to a deity
ishtapurta. A charitable act
Ishwara. God as Creator and Ruler
Ishwara pranidhara. Attention to God
itihāsa. Historical myth – history

jada. Of no intelligence
Janagni. The Fire of Wisdom
Jagatguru. A World Teacher
japa. The repetition of a holy name
japa mala. A string of beads used in japa, a rosary

jihvā. The subtle organ connected with the tongue (taste and speech)
jiva. The individual soul
jivan mukta. A liberated person
Jnāna. Spiritual knowledge
Jnāna Kānda. Scriptures relating to Jnana
Jnāna Yoga. The Yoga relating to Knowledge
jnanendriyas. The subtle organs of sensation (sight, sound, smell, taste and touch)
jalandhara. The throat lock
jammet. Incarnation
jyotis. The Inner Light

Kaivalya. Spiritual freedom
Kali-Yuga. The era in which we live; said to be a period of strife and over 5000 years gone
kalpa. A cycle of beginning and end
kāma-kānchana. Lust and greed
kamandel. A vessel for holy water
Kamya-karma. Optional rites
kapala bhāti. A breathing technique; literally "skull cleansing"
kārana. The subtle instrument of knowledge and action
kārana. The potential cause unmanifested
kārana-salila. Potential Cosmic Energy
karana-sharira. The causal body or "sheath of bliss"
karma. Action
Karma-kānda. That part of the Vedas dealing with ritual
karma-phala. The fruit of action
Karma Yoga. The Yoga of Action (cause and effect)
Karam-shaya. The mental receptacle of karmic effects
Karmavāda. The philosophy of cause and effect
karmendriyas. The subtle organs (indriyas) of action (hands, feet, etc.)
kārya. The effect or manifestation
khechari. A mudra in which the cavity in the roof of the mouth is sealed by the tongue
kirti. Frame
Kundalini. The "Serpent Power" or vital force coiled near the base of the spine
kleshas. The five sources of sorrow
kosha(s). Sheath(s) surrounding the soul (there are five, physical prana, mind, buddhi, sheath of bliss)
krama-mukti. Liberation in stages after death
kri. To act
Krishna. Divine Incarnation as Vishnu
Kriyā. An action for purification
kriyamāna. The future effect of present action

kshanti. Patience (a paramita)
kshastriya. A warrior (such as Arjuna)
kshiti. A bhuta, earth
kumbhaka. Breath retention associated with inhalation/exhalation

Lakshya. The final goal
Lingam. A phallic symbol
Linga-Sharira. The astral body
Laya Yoga. The Yoga of dissolution associated with Kundalini

madhura. A devotional attitude
mahākāvya. An epic
mahāpurusha. A highly spiritual person, a saint or sage
mahimā. Spiritual power
majjhim nikaya. The Middle Way
mamaga. The concept of "mine"
malapra yoga. A rosary of beads (shortened to "mala")
mandala. A square or circle design of occult significance; an aid to
    meditation
manana. The second step on the Path of Knowledge; deep reflection
manas. The intellectual faculty of mind
mānasa-puja. Worship in meditation
mānava-dharma. The essence of man (nature/religion)
manipūraka. The navel chakra
manomaya kosha. The mental sheath
mantra. A mystic word (or words) of power
mantrakāra. One able to formulate a mantra
Marga. A Path to Spiritual Attainment
matsyāsana. The "Fish" asan
māyā. Illusion
mayurasana. The "Peacock" asan
mithyachara. A sinner
moksha. Liberation from Samsara
mowna. A vow of silence
mudrā. Physical movements having occult effects
muktāsana. The "Liberation" pose
mukta-purusha. One who is spiritually liberated
mulādharā. The lowest chakra

nāda. An inner sound with mystic effects
nadis. Subtle nerve channels or currents
namah. A sign of greeting, a salutation
Nārāyana. A name of Vishnu
nāsikā. The subtle organ of smell (an indriya)
nauli. Exercise for the abdominal muscles

neti. Not "This" as opposed to "That", also an act of cleansing
nididhyāsana. The final step on the Path of Knowledge (meditation)
nidea. Sleep
nirākāra. Without form
nirlipta. Purity
nirguna. Without attributes (gunas)
nirodha. Mind control
nirvāna. The Buddhist goal; extinction of all personal desires and complete absorption into The One
nirvikalpa samadhi. A state of transcendence
nishedha. Unlawful action (see also Vidhi)
nishkampa. Service without thought of reward
nisreyasa. Supreme bliss
nitya pralnaya. Apparent dissolution during sleep
nitya karma. Daily rites
Nivritti-Marga. The Path of Renunciation
niyama. The second of the Eight Limbs of Yoga; moral discipline
nyasa. Ritual physical purification

Om. The sacred mantra having many meanings, principally associated with Brahman
Omkara. A form of "Om" representing Brahman

Padmāsana. The "Lotus" asan
panchikarana. The compounding of the five basic elements of the universe (bhutas)
pada. Feet
pani. Hands
pāpa. Evil deed; demerit
Pāpa purusha. An evil spirit
para. Supreme, the highest
para Bhakti. Supreme devotion
Parabrahman. The Absolute
Para Prakriti. Supreme Cosmic Energy
Paramātman. Supreme Spirit
Parameshwara. God
parināma. Transformation
Parinamavada. God transformed into His Universe; non-dualism
Paramita. The ten things leading to transcendence
Pārvati. The Divine Mother incarnated
Pashchimottāsana. The "Back Stretch" asan
pata. A picture
pauranika. Mythological
Pavriti Marga. The Path of Desire
paya. The organ of excretion

Phat. Force (as in explosion)
phatki. Firecracker
Pingala. The right-hand nerve channel along the spine
Pitriloka. The sphere of the manes
Pitri-yajna. Sacrifices to the manes
Prabdha-Karma. Ripe karma
prabuddha. Fully enlightened
Prakriti. Absolute Matter composed of the Gunas (Sattwa, Rajas, Tamas (equivalent to harmony, passion, inertia)
Prajāpati. A Hindu deity
prakshāra. Clarity, brightness
Pralaya. Dissolution of the universe (periodic)
pramada. Carelessness
Prāna. Vital energy, of five kinds, corresponding to the physiological functions
pranamaya kosha. The sheath of vital energy
Pranava. Another name for "Om"
Prānāyāma. Yoga breathing technique (one of the Eight Limbs of Yoga)
pranidhara. Surrender (a paramita)
pratyahara. Withdrawal of the senses
Prayaschitta Karma. Penance, of two kinds, asadhbrana (extraordinary) and sadharana (ordinary)
pratyatma. Satisfaction of desires
pratyavaya dosha. The sin of omission; unpleasant effects
praya. Wisdom
punya. Virtue; merit
Puraka. Inhalation, associated with kumbhaka and rechaka
Puranas. Mythological scriptures
Purusha. The essence of Spirit
Purushottama. The Supreme Lord

raga devesha. Likes and dislikes
Rāja Yoga. The Yoga of mental control
rajas. One of the three gunas (the quality of restlessness)
rajasika. Ambitions which have the quality of rajas
Rāma. God incarnated as Vishnu
rasa. Enjoyment; the sensation of taste
rechaka. Exhalation
ripu. Obstacles to Yoga; the passions (lust, greed, anger, jealousy conceit, infatuation)
Rishi. A Self-Realised Seer
rūpa. The sensation of seeing form or colour

sādhaka. One undergoing spiritual discipline
sādhanā. Religious practice in daily life

sadharana. Penance
saguna. That which has gunas (attributes)
Sah. He or That (Divinity)
sahaja. One's dharma due to previous karma
sahaj samadhi. Spontaneous ecstasy
sahasrara. The lotus in the skull (the "thousand-petalled")
sakya. One expressing friendship with God
sakama. Service with expectation of reward
sākārā. That which has form
sakshi. A witness
Salabhasana. The "Locust" asan
samadhana. Earnest seeking for spiritual attainment
samadhi. A transcendental state of bliss
samana. A vital air of the navel area
samatwam. Making no distinctions; equanimity
samchita. Past karma for future fruition
Samhitā(s). Sections of the Vedas dealing with hymns and rites
sampradaya. A particular sect
samsāra. Reincarnations
sanskāras. Impressions stored in the mind
samsriti. Repeated incarnations
samyama. A mental discipline of Raja Yoga (control of mind and senses)
Sankhya. An ancient system of Indian Philosophy (the Gita incorporates this in part)
santosha. Contentment
sanyama. Condition of mind during dhyana
sanyassa. Renunciation of worldly ties
sanyāssin. Monk
sara. Essence
sat. Being; Reality; a quality of Brahman
Sat-Chit-Ananda. Being – Consciousness – Bliss
sattwa. One of the three gunas (bland quality)
Savangasana. The Shoulder Stand (asan)
shabda. The principle of creative word or sound
Savasana. The "Corpse" asan
Shad-Darshana. The Six Systems of Hindu Philosophy
Shaiva. A sect worshipping God as Shiva
Shakta. God as Divine Mother
Shakti. Divine Power
shama. Mind control
Shankaracharya. An Indian Philosopher who founded the school of Advaita
shanti. Peace
shancha. Purity
sharira. The body (of three types, dense, subtle, causal)

Shastra(s). Hindu Scriptures
shabda. The sensation of sound
Shiva. God as Destroyer
shravana. The discipline of hearing the scriptures
shreyas. Ultimate bliss
shrota. The subtle organ of hearing
shudda. That which is pure
Shruti. Divine Revelation
shubha. Good
shunya. Void
Siddha. One who is liberated
siddhi(s). Occult powers
Siddhasana. The "adept" asan
sila. Discipline (a paramita)
Sirshasana. The Headstand asan
Smriti(s). Scriptures, other than Vedas
Sinhasana. The "Lion" asan
Soham. "I am Brahman"
sparsha. The sensation of touch
sraddha. Sustained faith
sravana. Listening to doctrines as preparation for meditation
sri. A form of address
Srishti. The Divine Creator as a projection of God
Sthiti. The universe in the period between its beginning and end
sthirata. Steady; unchanging
sthula. Physical or gross matter
sthula-sharira. The physical body
sudra. Servant or peasant caste
sukha. Happiness
sukshma. The subtle plane of existence
Sukhāsana. The "Pleasant" asan
sushumna. The central spinal nerve channel associated with ida and
    pingala
sushupti. Deep sleep
Sutra(s). Aphorisms; positive statements
swadharma. The Hindu code of duty
swadhishthana. The chakra in the reproductive area of the body
swaroopa. Personal nature
swādhayāya. Self-knowledge; study of scriptures
swar-loka. A heavenly region
swatandra. Independent
swarga. heaven
swarupa. One's true nature
swastika. An ancient symbol of good augury
Swastikasana. The "Auspicious" asan

tamas. A Guna; the quality of inertia, indolence or ignorance
tāmāsika. Ignorant
tanmātra(s). The elements forming the universe (bhutas)
Tantra(s). Scriptural Texts
tapas. Austerities performed for purification or penance
Tat-Twam-Asi. Thou art That
tattwa. A principle
tattwa-bodha. Freedom from karma; the essence of a thing
trātaka. An exercise for purifying and strengthening the eyes
trikona. The "Triangle" asan
trikuti. The space between the eyebrows
trigunātmika. Possessing the three gunas
twak. The subtle organ of touch (an indriya)

udāna. The vital air of the throat area and upwards
uddiyana. An asan for control of abdominal muscles
upādhi. One thing imposed upon another
Upanishad(s). Part of the Veda(s)
upāsana. Sitting in contemplation; worship
upashtam. The generative organs
upaya. Skill

vāda. Doctrine
vaidhi-bhakti. Devotional ritual
vairagya. Dispassion – unattracted by external desires
Vaishnava. A sect worshipping God as Vishnu
vaishya. The merchant caste
vak. Organ of speech
vanaprastha. The third stage of life; retirement; recluse
vajra. The irresistible (e.g. diamond or thunderbolt)
Vajrasana. The "Adamantine" asan
Vajroli. The "Thunderbolt" asan
vasti. Internal cleansing
vāyu. A vital air (a bhuta)
vedanā. The sensation of pain or impulse
Vedas. Ancient Indian Scriptures
Vedānta. The Philosophy of the Vedas or Upanishads
vibhuti(s). Supernormal powers
vichāra. Meditation
vidcha-mukti. Liberation after the present life
Vidhi. A Scriptural Commandment
vikalpa. Imagination
vikshipa. Mental turbulence
vijnānamaya-kosha. The sheath of buddhi
vipakas. Karmic reactions

viparitakarani. The "Inverted" asan
Virāsana. The "Hero" asan
Virat. The Creator manifested as the Universe (Macrocosm)
virya. Courage; energy (a paramita)
vishaya. The subtle organ of perception
vishosha. Special
Vishnu. God as Preserver
vishuddha. The throat chakra
vitarka. Perspicuity
viveka. Discrimination
Vrikasana. The "Tree" asan
vritti. A modification of chitta (mind stuff)
vyana. A vital air general to the body
vyashti. Individual

yajna. Sacrifice
Yajnavalka. A Sage named in the Upanishads
Yama. One of the Eight Limbs of Yoga (Observances)
Yantra. A design of occult significance
Yoga. Union; to yoke or to join
Yogarudha. Success in Yoga
Yogi. An aspirant for union with God

INDEX

Mukti, 53, 54, 110, 112
Muller, Professor, 28, 29
Muscles, 126, 128, 137, 140, 162

Nachiketas, 31
Naish Karma, 72
Naishyas, 191
Naka, 44
Naishkarma Siddhi, 190
Nervous System, 136–9, 145, 156,
    160
    Afferent, 138
    Autonomous, 138
    Central, 138
    Cranial, 138
    Efferent, 138
    Parasympathetic, 138
    Peripheral, 138
    Sympathetic, 138
Nirvana, 68, 69, 72
Nirvedananda, 120
Nivritti Marga, 119
Niyama, 91, 94, 125, 143, 145,
    151, 204
Nyaya, 22

Observances, 91, 93
Obstacles (to duty, etc.), 58, 91,
    99
OM, 35, 39, 42, 46, 69, 83
One, The, 18, 34, 36, 51, 52, 53,
    101, 149, 155, 200
Origen, 108
Oversoul, 114

Pain, 86, 88, 103
Pancharata Samhita, 24
Pandus, 48
Paramatman, 56
Pavarti, 30
Patanjali, 22, 48, 67, 71, 76–103,
    136, 206
Path of Action (Works), 50, 85
    Attainment, 71, 74, 80, 184,
    192

Desire, 116, 117, 119, 189
Devotion, 50, 178
    Knowledge, 50
    Self-Mastery, 50
    Renunciation, 119, 120
Pavlov, 139
Pavritti Marga, 116, 117,
    119
Perception, 52, 81, 89, 150,
    162–3, 169, 199
Period (Pleistocene, Permian,
    etc.), 128–9
Peristalsis, 135
Philosophy – The Six Classical
    Systems, 22, 27
Pippalada, 40
Power, 24, 45, 52, 56, 156, 172,
    175, 200
Powers, 41–2, 77, 90, 92, 93, 97,
    98, 99, 100
Practices, 77, 85, 88
Prakriti, 36, 46, 48, 51, 52, 57, 72,
    136
Prana, 41–3, 47, 56, 67, 92, 127,
    133, 145, 154, 155, 156, 158,
    201, 208
Pranayama, 84, 91, 94, 123, 151,
    157, 158, 205
Pratibha, 96, 97
Prayer, 166–87
Prayer, The Lord's, 176–8
Pratyahara, 91, 92, 94, 151,
    161–3, 205
Principles (of Man), 166.
    Appendix II
Principles of Belief, 202
Protoplasm, 126, 133
Psychosomatic, 85, 123
Puranas – Agni
    Bhagavata, 23
    Markendraya, 23
    Padma, 23
    Skanda, 23
    Vaya, 23
    Vishnu, 23